Nigel Dudley is a freelance enviro...
and writer. His previous publicatio...
Poisoned Earth, Nitrates and *The L*...
the organisations he has worked for ...
Earth, the Soil Association, Centre fo...
Technology, Earth Resources Resear... ...the London
Food Commission. He remains Project Director at the Soil
Association.

THE
SOIL ASSOCIATION
HANDBOOK

A CONSUMER GUIDE
TO FOOD, HEALTH
AND THE
ENVIRONMENT

NIGEL DUDLEY

First published in 1991 by
Macdonald Optima, a division of
Macdonald & Co. (Publishers) Ltd

A member of Maxwell Pergamon Publishing Corporation

British Library Cataloguing in Publication Data
Dudley, Nigel
 Soil Association Handbook.
 1. Food, related to health
 I. Title   II. Soil Association
 613.2

 ISBN 0-356-20041-8

Macdonald & Co. (Publishers) Ltd
Orbit House
1 New Fetter Lane
London EC4A 1AR

Typeset in Century Schoolbook by Leaper & Gard Ltd, Bristol

Printed and bound in Great Britain by
The Guernsey Press Co. Ltd., Guernsey, Channel Islands.

CONTENTS

ACKNOWLEDGMENTS

The author and publishers would like to thank the many people involved in helping make this book happen. In particular, Sue Stolton and Francis Cooper at the Soil Association, and David Symes for the copy editing.

1
INTRODUCTION: THE OLD AND THE NEW

As recently as the mid-1980s, many people probably hadn't heard the word 'organic' used in an agricultural context. And most people certainly wouldn't have suspected then that the Soil Association even existed. Yet paradoxically the popular picture today of the organic farmer or gardener is a traditionalist; someone who has turned back to the kind of farming practised before the Second World War.

Both suppositions are wrong. The Soil Association has been around since the 1940s, making it one of the oldest of today's environmental organisations. But organic farming itself isn't very much older than the Soil Association. Although it is based on some traditional methods of building soil fertility and controlling pests and diseases, it is also firmly founded on a modern scientific understanding of soil science, ecology and crop breeding, and it utilises many safe technological developments. This means that organic growing methods are still constantly evolving as farmers and market gardeners learn more about the systems. The Soil Association has a long history, but certainly not one without a lot of changes.

HOW AND WHY THE SOIL ASSOCIATION BEGAN

Green thinking did not start in the 1980s. Specific concerns about environmental problems can be traced back hundreds of years. However, it was during the 1930s that a number of important issues came to worry conservationists and progressive farmers, one of the most important of which was the massive amount of soil erosion taking place in many parts of the world as a result of bad farming practice. This soil erosion led, amongst other things, to the dustbowling in the United States that laid huge land areas to waste, the social effects of this early environmental disaster being movingly described in John Steinbeck's book *The Grapes of Wrath*. Another area of concern was the rapid intensification of agriculture, and the increasing reliance on artificial fertilisers, pesticides and heavy machinery. A few farmers and growers were already distrustful of these changes, 40-odd years before the current widespread criticism of our farming system. A handful of far-sighted doctors and dietitians also began speaking out against the changes that were taking place.

Lady Eve Balfour was one of the earliest pioneer organic farmers, although she didn't actually use the term herself for many years. Lady Eve started her farming career by training young girls to carry out farm work during the First World War. Immediately afterwards she bought her first farm, in Stowmarket, Suffolk, where she began her lifelong critique of intensive farming, and started developing practical alternatives. She also cut her campaigning teeth by successfully fighting against the unpopular tythe tax during the 1930s, and, by way of relaxation, played in a jazz band and wrote detective novels.

In 1943 Lady Eve published her book *The Living Soil*, in which she outlined her theories about the kind of agriculture that we now call 'organic'. The response to the book was so enthusiastic that she formed the Soil Association to help develop the ideas in practice. The first, and major, role of the Association was therefore to support the famous Haughley experiment, which tested out the developing principles of organic farming on a whole-farm scale. And Haughley, in rural Suffolk, remained the headquarters of the Soil Association for 40 years.

Lady Eve Balfour spelled out the scope of her interests in the preface to the first edition of *The Living Soil*:

> My subject is food, which concerns everyone; it is
> health, which concerns everyone; it is the soil, which
> concerns everyone – even if they do not realise it – and
> it is the history of certain recent scientific research
> linking these three vital subjects.

Lady Eve also spelled out the basic purpose of the Soil
Association in a few short sentences written for the first
ever issue of the organisation's journal, then called *Mother
Earth*, in 1946.

> People have begun to see life on this planet as a whole,
> and Nature's plan as a complicated system of
> interdependence rather than one based on competition.
> As an outcome of this interpretation of natural law, they
> share the belief that the only salvation for mankind lies
> in substituting co-operation for exploitation in all
> human activities from soil treatment to industrial and
> international relations ...
>
> Through the development of the new scientific
> techniques, a steady increase in our knowledge and
> understanding of Nature's biological laws and the
> significance of the complex interplay between living
> organisms must be brought about ...
>
> [The Soil Association], armed with real knowledge
> and the ability to interpret it, must use it to educate
> public opinion, not only regarding the need for a healthy
> soil – the source of our food – but also concerning the
> way in which that food should or should not be treated
> once it is grown; so that if people continue to abuse
> Nature's laws to their own detriment, or allow
> governments to do it for them, such behaviour shall at
> least be the outcome of an informed choice and not a
> blindfold and Gadarene descent into the abyss.

These ideas are expressed briefly, and famously, as the
relationship between soil, plant, animal and man.

The Soil Association has always been an environmental
organisation in the modern sense. But it has also had a
very practical function, in that many members rely on

making sure that the organic principles work well enough in practice to allow them to survive in the nitty gritty world of making a living as commercial organic growers and farmers. The Association was one of the first sources of hard information on these issues in Britain.

However, the Soil Association has always gone further than a simple, pragmatic approach to ecology. Throughout its history it has also considered the 'complicated system of interdependence' of the whole planet. Many of the ideas now discussed under the general umbrella of the Gaia principle were being talked about by the pioneers of the Soil Association in the 1940s. Indeed, some of the earliest ideas discussed by the Association still haven't really been worked through, and await proper investigation in the future.

CHANGES IN THE SOIL ASSOCIATION

The organic pioneers spent a long time out in the wilderness. The intensive farming system seemed unstoppable, buoyed up by technological optimism and, subsequently, fat cheques from the coffers of the European Community. After 30 years, the experimental farm at Haughley was closed down due to lack of funds, and the Soil Association was faced with a falling membership and an uncertain future.

However, at the same time, there was a new generation of organic farmers starting up in business. Many of them were people who had moved out into the country in the great exodus during the 1960s and 1970s, and who were already involved in the fledgling environmental groups like Friends of the Earth, Greenpeace and the anti-nuclear movement. Some of the local Soil Association groups took on a new lease of life. With the confidence of youth, determined to make a go of organic farming in a commercial market, and impatient with old fashioned ideas, the young turks of the organic movement gradually became more influential in the Soil Association nationally, making substantial changes to both the immediate priorities of the organisation and the way it was run.

The Soil Association of the 1980s therefore aimed at a higher-profile campaigning image. It started to take an active part in lobbying politicians, policymakers and conventional farmers about organic farming. It broadened its work into other areas, protesting about some of the major agricultural pollutants such as pesticide spray drift and nitrate pollution. And, crucially, it became involved in setting and administering the Soil Association standards for organic agriculture, which provided a consumer guarantee that food really was organic and, almost incidentally, defined exactly what 'organic' meant in Britain.

In 1985 the Association moved its headquarters to Bristol, losing a direct link with the countryside but becoming more accessible to visitors, the media and representatives from other organisations.

THE SOIL ASSOCIATION TODAY

Today the Soil Association is an active membership organisation, with 40 local groups and a staff of about a dozen in the Bristol headquarters. The Association's work is divided into a number of broad areas, which are outlined briefly below and discussed in much more detail in the main parts of the book.

Promotion of organic food and farming

The Soil Association is the largest organisation promoting organic farming in Britain. This involves everything from lobbying ministers and senior civil servants to persuading the everyday consumer that it is worth seeking out organic produce in his or her local shop or supermarket. Sales of organic food are already approaching £100 million a year in Britain, and rising fast. This is still a tiny proportion of the total food sales, of course, but analysts working for some of the major retailers believe that organic could account for 10 per cent of the food market by the end of the century. Almost all major retail stores in Britain, along with literally hundreds of smaller shops, now stock organic food; indeed, there isn't nearly enough organic food to satisfy demand.

Increasing the number of organic farms

The need for more organic food is now critical. The increase in demand is being met mainly by imports from mainland Europe, from Israel and, increasingly, from developing countries. But it doesn't make sense, from either an economic or an environmental point of view, to import crops that can easily be grown at home.

Accordingly, the Soil Association is involved in a campaign called '20 per cent organic by the year 2000', which seeks to convert a fifth of Britain's farmland to organic methods over the next decade. This involves working not only with the hundreds of individual farmers who are interested in going organic, but also with farming organisations, with other environmental groups, with animal welfare bodies, who are interested in organic meat because of the humane treatment of the animals, and with many members of parliament. Land under the Soil Association symbol increased sevenfold between 1985 and 1990, although it is still less than 1 per cent of agricultural land in the UK.

Maintaining a high standard of organic food

The increase in popularity and demand for organic food has meant that the chances of fraud have also increased; a minority of farmers could be tempted to grow conventional food and sell it as 'organic' to get the price premium. There has been at least one case of someone being successfully prosecuted for selling food labelled as organic on a market stall, when in fact it had received post-harvest treatment with pesticides.

In order to guard against deliberate or accidental malpractice, the Soil Association runs the famous Soil Association symbol scheme. Farmers and growers belonging to the scheme have to keep to the strict Soil Association standards for agriculture, which explain precisely what is and is not permitted in organic growing. These standards are doubly important; not only do they help to provide a consumer guarantee that food is genuinely organic, but also, because no one had really defined what organic agriculture actually was before, they set down a set of clear guidelines for the practice of organic agriculture. The standards are constantly under review, and they change as we learn more about the farming systems and their effects. They have been adopted virtually unchanged by the British government for their own umbrella set of organic standards.

A consumer watchdog on food, health and environment

Since the early 1980s the Soil Association has also built up a reputation as a campaigning organisation focusing on issues relating to food, farming and health. It has sponsored research, published pamphlets and reports, and carried out local and national lobbying on a range of issues, including:

- Pesticide spray drift.
- Garden pesticides.
- The incidence of soil erosion in Britain.
- Nitrate pollution of freshwater and vegetables.
- Food additives.
- Pesticide residues in food.
- Aerial spraying.
- The 'safe meat' campaign.
- Air pollution and agriculture.

But the Soil Association is unusual amongst campaigning organisations in that it starts from a positive basis of promoting a safer alternative. This means that all the campaigns, whilst they may be critical of specific practices, are not just saying 'No' to something without any practical alternatives in mind. For example, if the Soil Association complains about pesticide residues in food, it is able to offer a proven farming system that doesn't rely on pesticides. And importantly, because many Soil Association members are farmers, we don't usually fall into the trap of 'farmer bashing' as a way of explaining the problems of the countryside or of food.

Information and education

None of the above counts for much if the ideas are not put across to the people who matter, be they MPs or school students. Accordingly, the Association produces a large amount of educational material, ranging from children's teaching kits to slide sets, pamphlets to books. There are regularly updated guides on where to buy organic food, consumers' reference books on a range of issues including garden pesticides and additives, discussion documents, papers, reprints and a regular journal, *Living Earth*.

HOW TO USE THIS BOOK

This book is intended as both an introduction to the Soil Association's activities and a reference book for people who are interested in good food and a clean environment. The first part looks at some current problems associated with food and farming, including both those that damage the environment and those that effect our own health, or those of children, the elderly and other groups particularly at risk. Next, there is an introduction to organic farming and gardening. This should help not only people who are interested in knowing exactly what organic farming means in practice but also those who want to find out about how to start organic gardening themselves. A resources section explains where to get further information, assistance and, naturally, how to find organic food.

THE CONSUMER'S GUIDE TO FOOD, HEALTH AND THE ENVIRONMENT

After years of congratulating ourselves on the quality of British food and farming, both are now coming in for increasing criticism from consumers, politicians, environmentalists and from farmers' organisations. This criticism falls into four main areas:

- Food is no longer perceived to be as good as it once was, both because of the ways it is produced and processed, and because of mounting fears about a range of diseases and contaminants getting into our diet.
- Farming is, often unwittingly, contributing to environmental pollution and the destruction of the countryside.
- Farm animals are being treated extremely badly in many cases. Even people who are not vegetarians are concerned about some aspects of factory farming and the treatment of livestock.
- Modern farming methods are contributing to global environmental and social problems.

Not all the horror stories are true of course. Most farmers, and food processors, are as worried about what is happening as everyone else. Farmers are facing enormous threats from falling demand, risks to grant aid, and changing public perceptions of what farming should have to offer. They are increasingly controlled by the whims of government, in Britain and Europe, which frequently puts short term political gain ahead of longer term sustainable environmental policies. There is enormous confusion in the farming world about what may happen in the future.

And all this communicates itself straight back to fears about the quality of the food on your plate.

For anyone worried about what is going on, it is sometimes difficult to know where to turn for clear unbiased information, or what to do to make sure that you get the best, and healthiest, food possible. Reacting to the latest scare being hyped up by the media is not necessarily the best policy. The following section of the manual therefore looks at the four main issues outlined above. It gives a brief overview of the facts and debate, and suggests things we can all do to help improve matters. More detailed sources of information are listed in the resources section at the end of the book.

2
WHAT'S ON MY PLATE?

Food isn't like it used to be. How often have we heard our parents and grandparents grumbling about the taste and quality of food today, and comparing it with that of the good old days? And they're dead right. Anyone reading this book who grew up before the Second World War will be able to remember for themselves. For all the massive expenditure on food processing, agricultural research, marketing and flavourings, the actual taste and quality of our food have declined. This section of the book tells you why. We look at contaminants in food (both deliberate and accidental); at old and new food poisoning; at processing methods that damage food; and, last but by no means least, at the ways in which the quality and variety of food have been deliberately reduced.

PESTICIDES UNDER THE SKIN

Every year about a billion gallons of pesticide-containing spray are used on British crops. Over 200 chemicals are available, of which at least 50 are known to be involved with, or suspected of, causing cancer. Others promote allergies, birth defects and other health problems. A proportion of these pesticides remain as residues on food; some will be on the outside, where they can be washed off, but other systemic pesticides become incorporated into the plant, and persistent pesticides can build up in the bodies of farm animals and be passed on to us in dairy products and meat.

Until recently it was believed that there were few pesticide residues on or inside food in Britain, but research over the last few years has proved this to be wrong. In 1989 a government survey found pesticides on virtually all kinds of food, including vegetables, fruit, grains, meat and dairy products. Mother's breast milk also frequently contains residues of persistent pesticides. The government spokesman who presented the results at a press conference stated bluntly that 'there is no such thing as pesticide free food' in the UK.

The problem can be even worse when food is imported. Although some of the most hazardous pesticides have now been banned in Britain, such as the persistent organochlorines like DDT, they are still frequently used in other countries, especially in the developing world. (Not infrequently, these chemicals are still manufactured in the west, and sold for export, long after they have been banned here.) This means that food imported from countries with less stringent pollution regulations is at risk of even higher levels of pesticide residues. Therefore, many of the 'health foods' sold in Britain, such as grains, pulses and nuts, contain significant quantities of pesticides. Exporting pesticides and importing pesticide residues on food has become known as the circle of poison.

The government now argues that, although there are pesticides on many foods, the levels are far too small to matter. (Indeed, by very definition, residues are usually very small.) However, we simply don't know enough about health effects to be sure as yet; there has been very little research into the effects of continual doses of very small amounts of particular pesticides, and almost no research at all on the effects of mixtures of many different pesticides. Some of these have effects on the immune system, for example, and have been identified as a possible contributory cause of ME (myalgic encephalomyelitis, or chronic fatigue syndrome). Others could help stimulate allergic responses, particularly in view of the fact that food allergies are currently increasing fast.

Many older pesticides currently in use were licensed before there was very careful testing of health effects.

Although these are supposed to be retested regularly, we simply don't have the staff or money in Britain to carry out the tests fast enough; this is a state of affairs that has drawn complaints from both the agrochemical industry and the environment movement.

Other countries remain more cautious in their approach to pesticide residues on food; at least 40 chemicals currently in use in Britain have been banned in at least one other country for health reasons. In the United States the National Resources Defense Council (NRDC) calculated that 6,000 of the current pre-school children in America would die of cancer caused by pesticide residues on 15 major food crops. They identified a number of pesticides as being particularly harmful, including alar (chemical name daminozide), which is used on apples and can turn up in 'pure' apple juice. The NRDC is a non-governmental organisation, but its concern has been mirrored by the United States Environmental Protection Agency (US EPA), which has insisted that alar be withdrawn, and is investigating three other chemicals identified by the NRDC – maneb, macozeb and zineb. Despite a high-profile campaign against its use in the UK, alar was again given the all-clear by the British government in 1990. (In fact this decision is fairly meaningless, in that alar has been withdrawn worldwide in a voluntary ban by its manufacturers.) The other pesticides are still used here (and are also sold as garden chemicals).

Under pressure from the European Community, the British government has introduced maximum residue limits (MRLs) for pesticides. This is the maximum amount of pesticide allowed on food sold for eating. However, MRLs haven't been set for all pesticides because our current levels are simply too high to meet European standards. Although the standards are set according to internationally accepted criteria, because we know so little about the long term effects of small doses of pesticides on the body, all the MRLs are fairly arbitrary anyway.

Even if the MRLs are actually set, and really are safe, it is very difficult to be sure that they are being met in practice. The small amount of time and money the government puts into monitoring pesticide levels makes it easy for deliberate or accidental abuse of the laws to take place. Very few samples are taken on a national level, and only a fairly small proportion of the pesticides that may be present are actually tested for. Indeed, good tests don't even exist for all the pesticides that might be encountered. This problem was identified in parliament by the House of Commons Select Committee on Agriculture, who wrote in a 1986 report that:

> Although MAFF [The Ministry of Agriculture, Fisheries and Food] claims to analyse a large number of products which might contain pesticide residues, this represents a very low proportion of monitoring bearing in mind the number of approved pesticides. *We do not believe that this is enough to encourage compliance with good agricultural practice.* (our emphasis)

The Soil Association has campaigned against pesticide residues for years. Although organic food is likely to have lower pesticide residues than conventional food, the existence of spray drift (see pages 51–2) and persistent pesticides, which can remain in the soil for years, we cannot ever guarantee that any food grown in the industrialised world will be completely free of pesticides. Research in Germany suggests that about 3 per cent of guaranteed organic food will contain pesticide residues as a result of spray drift, long term soil contamination, etc.

In 1989 the Soil Association therefore published a ten-point plan for cleaning up our food, including the following:

- A number of the most hazardous pesticides should be withdrawn immediately.
- Maximum residue limits (MRLs) should be set for all pesticides used in Britain, and not just those the government thinks will not consistently show up as over the maximum.

- Staff and resources for testing for pesticide residues in food should be increased, especially for imported food, if the MRL system is to be effective.
- Fruit and vegetables sold in shops should be labelled with the pesticide used both during growth and after harvest.
- Penalties for causing spray drift must be increased, to reduce accidental contamination of crops, and the process of claiming damages should be speeded up.
- All pesticide exports should be subject to prior informed consent, whereby buyers are told about possible health risks and restrictions in the country of origin. This will help reduce the re-import of hazardous pesticides in food.
- A full scale epidemiological study (i.e. a health study on a large human population, taking all factors into careful account) is required into the possible impact of low levels of pesticide residues on our health.
- A large education campaign is required to teach consumers and farmers about how to minimise the hazards of pesticide residues.
- Far more research funding is needed to investigate the potential for non-chemical methods of pest and weed control.
- Proper government support is required for organic agriculture, particularly with respect to support over the period of conversion from chemical to organic methods, if public demand for organic food is to be met.

Our plan was dismissed in terms such as 'immature and impractical' by some commentators when it was first published. But a lot has changed since then. Virtually all the points have now been echoed by official and international bodies. For example, the British Agrochemicals Association has called for extra staff and resources for testing; the Food and Agricultural Organisation of the United Nations is introducing prior informed consent; the European Commission is lobbying for Britain to introduce MRLs; and the far from radical

British Medical Association, in a widely publicised report released in October 1990, called for pesticide labelling on food in shops.

But despite this definite change in attitude, very little action is forthcoming on these points. So for the time being, if you are worried about pesticides on food, our advice is that you should buy organic if possible. Failing that, wash food thoroughly, as this will remove some of the pesticides. Peeling fruit and vegetables also helps, because pesticides are often concentrated in the skin; but unfortunately, so too is much of the goodness, and nutritionists have spent years advising us to leave on skin. If you are making marmalade, or using lemons in drinks, you should buy fruit specifically labelled for those purposes, because other citrus fruit has wax and pesticides on the skin.

- **Consumer tip**. Remember that some of the highest pesticide residues can be found on wholefoods like brown bread, brown rice and some pulses, precisely because they haven't been processed to remove the outer layer. It is certainly worth buying these organically grown if at all possible.

A HIGH NITRATE DIET

Pesticides are not the only agrochemicals to end up in our food and drink. Nitrate levels are rising in both drinking water and many foodstuffs, and are causing ripples of concern throughout the European Community.

Nitrate is essential for plant growth. In organic farming it is supplied to the soil by leguminous crops (members of the pea and bean family), which have bacteria in their roots capable of 'fixing' nitrogen from the air (i.e. the bacteria convert nitrogen in the air to nitrate in the soil). Other important sources include careful use of composts and manures. But in intensive farming, nitrate is supplied as artificial fertilisers, usually in a soluble form.

Intensive farming has resulted in a great increase in

nitrate losses from farmland. This occurs when fertilisers run off fields or leach downwards into groundwater; when fields are ploughed up; and when large amounts of slurry or manure are applied to the land, or leak out of slurry tanks. There is still a lot of argument about exactly which stage of the farming process causes the bulk of these losses, but it is now accepted that intensive chemical farming means extra nitrate in the environment.

Some of this nitrate then ends up in our diet, from three main sources:

- Drinking water. Nitrate levels in the drinking water of many agricultural areas of Britain are now above the limits set by the European Commission. Nitrate is polluting both surface water and underground aquifers (which supply a third of Britain's drinking water). Over a million people already drink water that exceeds EC and World Health Organisation nitrate limits for at least part of the year.
- Vegetables. Modern cultivation methods can increase nitrate levels in crops, especially when they are grown under glass in the winter. This seems to be because plants build up nitrate in their tissues for growth later in the season and, if they are picked while still growing, these high nitrate concentrations can reach the dining table. Some plants build up higher nitrate levels than others; spinach and lettuce are both well known for this. There is also some evidence that more modern varieties, grown with artificial fertilisers, have even higher nitrate levels. The UK has no legal limits on nitrate levels, but research by Elm Farm Research Centre showed that nitrates in British lettuces sometimes exceed maximum levels permitted in countries such as Austria, the Netherlands and Switzerland.
- Meat. Nitrate is deliberately added to meat to protect against botulism (a form of bacterial food poisoning). There are thought to be acceptable alternatives available, but very little research on this appears to have been carried out.

The proportion of nitrate coming from different sources depends on where you live. In high nitrate areas over half the nitrate will come from water, although in most other circumstances nitrate in food will provide the most. Other foodstuffs, including dairy products, also contribute to the total amount of nitrate consumed; for example, potatoes are quite a major source, not because they contain particularly high levels, but because they form such a large proportion of many people's diets.

There are a number of environmental problems with high nitrate levels, especially when they occur in water (see page 48), but the main focus of concern has been on the effects nitrate can have on human health. At the moment, international safety standards are set to avoid the risk of methaemoglobinaemia, otherwise known as blue baby syndrome; this is a potentially fatal blood disorder that can affect bottle-fed infants, especially those less than three months old, in areas where there are high nitrate levels in drinking water. However, it is a very rare complaint. There have only been a handful of cases in Britain, with one known death, and the last reported incident was in the early 1970s. Methaemoglobinaemia is likely to be a much more significant problem in countries where high nitrate levels are combined with poor hygiene and malnutrition. That said, the increasing nitrate levels in Europe are giving cause for concern, and in some places nursing mothers are provided with bottled water by their local water company.

A much more serious worry is the suspicion that nitrate could be linked to the development of stomach cancer. Nitrate can break down into the body, first to nitrite, which in turn forms nitrosamines. Nitrosamines are powerful carcinogens (cancer promoters) in a large number of laboratory animals, including some monkeys and apes. However, detailed epidemiological studies have so far failed to find any very clear link in humans.

The agrochemical industry has made much of this research, using it to back up their claims that nitrate is completely safe, but the researchers themselves are usually more cautious. There may be different reactions, depending on how the nitrate is taken in; for example most vegetables also contain vitamin C, which is supposed to help prevent stomach cancer, so the two effects could be cancelling each other out. In addition, nitrate levels are continuing to rise steeply in some areas, and in some foods, so that there may be effects at higher concentrations that just haven't shown up yet in mortality statistics.

The Soil Association has campaigned on nitrate in a number of ways, including the promotion of organic farming as a means of reducing nitrate leaching from farmland (see page 87) and asking for maximum residue limits to be introduced for nitrate in food, in line with other European countries. Over the last few years, the British government has received a lot of criticism from the EC for its lack of a proper policy for reducing nitrate levels; this has resulted in the government being taken to the European Court on more than one occasion.

The need to reduce nitrate in water in many agricultural areas has given a much needed boost to the organic option. But for the time being, if you are worried about nitrate in food and water, there are a few simple steps that can reduce the problem. Some water filters remove nitrate, but always check carefully with the manufacturers before buying, because many do not, and those that do work often need the filter to be changed fairly frequently. Boiling does not get rid of nitrate. Mineral water probably contains less nitrate, although it is expensive if used for all drinking water (including tea, coffee, and so on).

- **Consumer tip**. There is no simple way of telling if vegetables have high nitrate levels. However, as the highest levels are likely to be found in those grown out of season, it may be worth avoiding high-risk crops such as spinach and lettuce at times when they will only be available if grown under glass. In addition, some organic and free range meats may not contain nitrate preservatives.

ADDING TO THE PROBLEM

It is not just accidental additions to the diet that are causing concern to health conscious people in Britain. There are also increasing worries about the huge number of food additives that arrive, with little explanation, in our food. Additives is a catch-all word that includes colourings (dyes), preservatives, a range of stabilisers and (by far the most numerous) flavourings. And most of us eat between 3 and 7 kilograms of chemical additives in our diet every year; some people may eat up to 15 kilograms.

A survey carried out a few years ago by the Consumers' Association found that over half the people in Britain thought that all additives are tested for safety before being used. They are not. Somewhat over 300 additives are regulated and have identification numbers; quite a lot of these are also regulated by the European Community, whereupon they also get an E prefix. Thus E100 is turmeric, a dye and flavouring commonly used in Asian cooking; the E and the 100 means that it has been regulated by both the European Community and Britain. The additive 107, on the other hand, is another dye, Yellow 2G, which has not been listed by the EC (and, in fact, is banned in at least 10 countries, including Denmark, France and the USA), but which is still permitted in Britain.

So far so good. People buying food can see additives listed, frequently by both name and E number, on the label. Unfortunately, there are still two problems. First, there are about 3,500 additives used in Britain, i.e. over ten times the number that are actually regulated. The vast majority are flavourings; many of these are probably completely safe, but there are a growing number of completely artificial 'flavours', often mimicking recognisable flavours, about which we know very little.

Secondly, there are still a lot of permitted additives that are suspected of having a range of health effects, and which have been banned by a number of other countries. These health effects include risks of cancer; indeed, some medical authorities now identify food additives as one of the major causes of cancer in the developed world. But another side effect that has become particularly well known over the past few years is the strongly suspected link between hyperactivity in children and certain food additives, including the azo dyes, cochineal and benzoates amongst others. Examples of other problems include links between migraines and propiniates; skin allergies and stearates; and aluminium and the form of premature senility known as Alzheimer's disease.

But even if an additive has crossed the hurdle of the European Commission and has been awarded an E number, it does not necessarily mean that everyone is happy about its safety. For example, the dyes Black PN (E151), used in blackcurrant jam and cheesecake, and Patent Blue (E131), used in ice cream, sweets and processed peas, have both been banned in Norway and the United States, although they are permitted in the European Community. Globally, the situation is thus a complete mess.

Understandably many people are nowadays becoming cautious about additives, and manufacturers are responding by removing some of the more controversial types. However, watch out for misleading information. Packets that tell you 'Preservative Free' or 'No Artificial Colourings' may well have other additives, details of which you have to hunt for in the small print on the label.

Although there are now complicated (and apparently constantly changing) rules regulating what can or cannot appear on a food label, they are not much good unless you understand them. For example, if a tin says 'raspberry flavoured' and there is a picture of a raspberry on the tin, it means that the food must contain at least some raspberries. But if it says 'raspberry flavoured' and there is no raspberry picture, it may well only contain a chemical that tastes (roughly) like raspberry. Not many people know that.

The other important thing to bear in mind is that it is not only artificial chemical additives that can cause

problems. You should also avoid eating too much of the
common natural ingredients such as sugar and salt, as we
explain on pages 23–4. Some natural products have known
or suspected health effects; for example, carrageenan, the
edible seaweed also known as Irish moss, may cause
ulcerative colitis, and may decompose into a carcinogen.

In 1984 Bill Horner and Dr Peter Mansfield prepared a
report for the Soil Association that looked at all the listed
chemicals available at the time. Called *Look Again at the
Label*, in deliberate reference to the government's
pamphlet *Look at the Label*, it identified over 100
additives used in Britain which were actually or
potentially harmful. Three years later, the Consumers'
Association published a book in which they, more
cautiously, listed 58 'which you may wish to avoid'.
Despite all the publicity, new additives, especially
flavourings, appear on the market all the time, and
hundreds are awaiting evaluation.

Fortunately, there are now plenty of sources of additive
free food; additive free fast foods or convenience foods are
harder to come by, although there are now some available.
Organic food is usually sold in as natural a state as
possible and should never have any dangerous or
unnecessary additives. The same is true for most
non-organic components of wholefood shops. The cardinal
rule in all cases is to read the label carefully, including the
small print, and taking notice of any sly reference to
'flavourings' (which don't have to be identified by law).

SWEET TOOTHLESS

It is not just the additives with long chemical names that
should be treated with caution. Two of the most universal
additives – sugar and salt – can be highly hazardous to our
health if they are taken in excess.

Sugar
Let's consider sugar first. Refined sugars do not provide
much in the way of nutrition. They give a sudden burst of

energy, but this is followed by a low, just like many other addictive drugs. They also contribute enormously to being overweight, to tooth decay and to a host of other ailments. British people currently eat about a 100 pounds of sugar a year per person (which means that some people eat far more); this is about 50 big bags of sugar a year, or about a packet a week. The National Advisory Committee on Nutritional Education advises that we should halve this intake. But this is not as easy as it sounds. You can certainly reduce sugar intake by not adding it to tea and coffee, or by cutting down on sweets, cakes and chocolate. But sugar is added, much more subtly, to other foods as well.

Food labels are supposed to list ingredients in order of quantity, i.e. the largest constituent is put first. Try taking a look at the constituents of a whole range of foods, from fizzy pop through biscuits to baked beans, and you will find sugar at or near the number one place. Up to 15 per cent of a can of baked beans can be sugar. Most breakfast cereals contain sugar. Jam, by law, has to contain at least 60 per cent sugar in order to be called 'jam' at all. Tinned fruit, vegetables and soups are all likely to have sugars added.

Watch out, also, for the small print. Not many manufacturers write 'sugar' nowadays, as the word has got around that too much sugar makes all your teeth fall out and makes you fat. Labels therefore generally break down the overall sugar content into its constituent parts – which may also have the advantage of taking it off the top position. The most common sugars you will see are glucose, sucrose, fructose and maltose. But, they're all sugar.

Many supposedly 'healthy' foods are stuffed with sugar as well. The average tub of yoghurt contains four teaspoonfuls of sugar. Many of the muesli bars now on sale actually have higher sugar ratings than the traditional chocolate bars, according to a survey by the London Food Commission. Fruit juices can have up to 15 grams of sugar added per litre before they have to be labelled as 'sweetened', and even those that do not contain added sugars may be so concentrated that the natural sugars have reached wholly unnatural levels. Sugar has now suffused our diets so thoroughly that it is only the people who make a conscious effort who are able to avoid eating large amounts of it.

So if you want to cut down your sugar intake, you have to think quite carefully about what you eat. Most fresh foods are fine, but any processed food is likely to have sugar added, and to find out how much you'll have to check the label – some brands and some retail stores now have a policy of putting detailed nutritional information on the packet. There are also a growing number of brands, including many organic foods, that deliberately cut down on sugar.

- **Consumer tip**. Sugar is addictive. Anyone who gets a craving for sweets, chocolate, sugar in tea and so on is (probably mildly) addicted to sugar. Like other addictive drugs – the ones with more menacing names – taking a sudden burst of sugar gives you a quick buzz and then makes you feel low again as your energy levels fall off. If you want to eat less sugar, you have to go cold turkey and wean yourself off gradually. And it can be quite a painful process.

Salt
The same is also true for salt. We do need a certain amount of salt in our diet, but nowhere near as much as most people consume. The old adage about requiring salt tablets in the tropics isn't normally true either; the body quickly acclimatises to hotter weather and releases less salt in the heat. Salt is linked to the development of high blood pressure, which itself can lead to heart attacks. Worldwide studies have found that societies that eat large amounts of salt (and fats) tend to have high blood pressures, while societies that have neither do not have problems with high blood pressure. British people, on average, eat two to four times as much salt as

recommended as the upper limit by the World Health Organisation.

But again, as in the case of sugar, salt is added constantly to our food, whether we like it or not. Salt is still used as a preservative (which was necessary in the past when other methods of preservation were not available); it is added to margarines; it is found in breakfast cereals; and it is in canned vegetables. Then, of course, there are the foods that are made salty especially to increase your thirst, such as the potato crisps and salted nuts sold in pubs and bars.

JUST ADD WATER

Even when additives aren't actually harmful to health, they can still affect food quality. Take water for example. Water occurs naturally in all living things – humans are 50–60 per cent water, for example. Water becomes a problem, though, when the amount in food is accidentally or deliberately increased. For a start it means that, weight for weight, you get less for your money. And many modern food processing techniques deliberately increase the amount of water in food so that you have to buy more to get sufficient nutrition.

But surely, you might say, this is a bit pedantic? No it isn't. Ever since the 1960s consumers have been ripped off by manufacturers who add polyphosphates (E450) to meat and fish products, to increase their water content. Although manufacturers claim a range of benefits from polyphosphates, including improved eating quality, the main advantage to them is that the products weigh more, and therefore can be sold for more. The London Food Commission worked out that about £6 million worth of water is sold every year in Britain in fish fingers alone. The same is true for poultry that are wet chilled; a survey carried out in Shropshire in 1986 found water content varying from 6 to 17 per cent. Use of the Chorleywood bread-making process (responsible for three-quarters of Britain's loaves) increases water content in bread as well;

research by the Food Additives Campaign Team and the Consumers Association estimated that additional water in bread from this method costs us £15 million a year. Some cooked cured meats contain more water than solid matter. Water is therefore big business to Britain's food manufacturers today.

Water also builds up in foods if they are grown in intensive agriculture systems. Use of soluble nitrate fertilisers leads to rapid growth in vegetables and grains, but tends to increase their water content at the same time. This means that chemically produced food contains, weight for weight, less nutritive value than organically produced food. Yet all comparisons between the two systems are based on total weight produced. If you buy a huge rapidly grown carrot it may look very impressive, but it is unlikely to taste as good as a smaller slower grown specimen, and it probably won't contain as many nutrients, weight for weight.

Issues surrounding water in food have been scarcely discussed in Britain, which is a pity, because most consumers are paying a proportion of their weekly food bill for something that they could get hold of a great deal more easily by just turning on the tap.

MEDICATION WITHOUT ILLNESS

Meat and dairy products can contain other unwanted additives in the form of antibiotics and artificial hormones, although the latter are illegal in Europe at the moment.

Let's consider hormones first. Hormones are natural chemical substances, made in the various glands of the body. They play a complex role in our life and effectively act as regulatory chemicals which control things like rate of growth, milk production, sexual function, and so on. But chemists are now able to manufacture many artificial hormones, which can be used by the farmer to help control animals' behaviour, growth rate, sexuality and milk production. For example, artificial hormones can:

- Ensure that all female animals come on heat at the same time, allowing the breeding programme to go more smoothly.
- Induce miscarriages to increase growth rate in female cattle.
- Artificially 'castrate' pigs and cockerels.
- And, by far the most important, make the animals put on weight more quickly.

Artificial hormones have been withdrawn in the EC, although there is, by all accounts, still a flourishing black market. The ban came after revelations of a range of health effects in both humans and animals. Some of these, involving hormones that are now no longer legally available, have become notorious; one region of Costa Rica, for example, had girls as young as three or four starting to become sexually mature, developing breasts and pubic hair, and starting menstruation, and many went on to develop ovarian cysts a few years later.

Most artificial hormones are fortunately nothing like so dangerous. However, the range of health effects, and the fact that many of them have bad effects on the welfare of the animals, caused the European Community to introduce a ban, despite objections from Britain. This caused bitter opposition from the United States, Australia and New Zealand, where artificial hormones are still used on a vast scale. And it may become illegal to impose the ban if new international trade laws are agreed, in which case we may, once again, face hormone-laced meat in Britain.

But even if we do not, our meat still ends up with a lot of added rubbish in it. The ways in which animals are kept (described in chapter 4) mean that many more become ill than they would if they led a more natural healthy existence. Many animals are kept going with constant medication, and the same antibiotics that were once used as growth promoters are now used to counter stress. Vets often do not look too carefully at exactly what quantities of antibiotics are administered; the editor of the *Veterinary Record* writing in 1985, stated bluntly that 'The emphasis has shifted from [antibiotic] use as growth promoters to prophylaxis to counter the stress imposed on calves by modern practice in the calf industry.' In other words, business as usual.

The Soil Association has long led the fight against over-use of antibiotics. Although they are allowed in Soil Association standard animals if they are ill, most routine 'precautionary' uses are banned, and the animals must have a much longer detoxification period before they are sold as meat. This has produced a barrage of criticism from the veterinary industry, which has accused the Soil Association of cruelty to animals because, they claim, the animals will suffer more ill health. The experience of the many practising organic livestock farmers is that the reverse is actually the case; without undue stress, unnatural food and forced growth, animals stay healthier and need less medication.

- **Consumer tip**. There is now a growing variety of meat available that hasn't been overdosed with all sorts of unnecessary drugs and hormones. This is described in the section on organic meat on page 80.

IRRADIATION – A NEW USE FOR NUCLEAR ENERGY

Another way in which the food industry has been trying to get around the bad press surrounding additives is by replacing preservatives with the technique of irradiation. In a food irradiation plant, foodstuffs are exposed to short intense bursts of ionising radiation from radioactive isotopes. This helps preserve the food in a number of ways. Bacteria are killed instantly, as are many insect pests (or, if the insects aren't actually killed, they will be made sterile so that they cannot breed). Irradiation can also delay the ripening of fruit, so that it can be stored for much longer periods and shipped further afield; the food still looks the same, and will stay fresh for much longer periods. Irradiation improves the baking characteristics of wheat, increases yields in wine and beer making, and speeds up the process of cooking dried vegetables. Once irradiated, the food doesn't contain any radioactivity.

At the moment irradiation is being considered for fish, chicken, grains, bread, vegetables and many types of fresh fruit, and is already being used in many countries for such produce as potatoes, onions, garlic, beans, apples and other fruit, dried fish, shrimp, chicken, dried egg, pulses, rice, spices and black pepper. Other foods have been cleared for use – irradiation is often used on herbs and spices, for example.

At first sight, irradiation looks like the answer to the food industry's prayers, and it also provides a huge potential source of income for the ailing nuclear industry, which has understandably been active in promoting the technique. Many large and influential organisations, including the World Health Organisation and the European Community, have spoken out in favour of food irradiation. However, food irradiation has raised more questions than it has answered from the health and safety point of view, and proposals for introducing it have met with staunch opposition from consumer groups, many food retailers and a surprising number of food writers and experts.

The first concern is that irradiation could increase the amounts of toxic chemicals found in food. Bombarding food with radiation can change its chemical structure; for example, fats and oils usually become rancid after being irradiated, and irradiation is not currently being considered for meat or dairy products because of this. There is widespread concern that similar chemical changes could result in some cancer-causing chemicals being created.

Some scientists at the National Institute of Nutrition at Hyderabad, India, claimed to have found a link between irradiated wheat and both cancer and immune deficiency in test animals. Their research has been heavily criticised by some researchers in the west and has been the subject of repeated attacks. However, as Tony Webb and Tim

Lang show in their book *Food Irradiation: The Myth and the Reality*, the basic data have never been effectively repudiated.

There are also doubts about how effective irradiation will be at controlling bacteria in everyday use. Experiments have already shown that bacteria resistant to irradiation can evolve, for example in the case of *Salmonella* species. Even if we ignore the possibility of resistance developing, irradiation destroys all bacteria, regardless of whether they are harmful or beneficial. This means that if food is subsequently re-infected with a harmful bacteria, this species will have a clear run and will be able to breed without competition, thus causing a serious health problem. (The same general problems are seen in the case of pasteurised milk, as explained on pages 38, 98–9).

The second major concern is that, even supposing irradiated food is safe, it may not have the same nutritional value as fresh food. Polyunsaturated fats are changed by the irradiation process, and may lose some of their nutritional value. There is good evidence that vitamin levels are also reduced. This is especially significant because irradiation is most likely to be used on produce such as fresh fruit and vegetables, which are precisely the foods that most people choose in order to obtain sufficient quantities of vitamins.

There are other related safety problems. Whilst it is true that irradiation doesn't leave radioactive food, it does result in increasing amounts of radioactive waste from the irradiation plants, and it does pose real health risks to the people who work in those plants.

Perhaps the real problem with food irradiation, though, is that it is attempting to provide a single technical fix to try and solve a whole range of complicated food problems, which are themselves a result of the intensive food production processes. Professor Richard Lacey, of Leeds University, summed up the problem by saying 'Food irradiation is an irrelevancy. Far from solving food problems it could add to them'.

At one time it looked as if irradiated food would not even be very adequately labelled, and the British government was proposing that there be no obligation to identify food as having been irradiated. However, there was such an outcry from consumer groups that this point has now been conceded, and all irradiated food sold will bear a label like the one shown.

- **Consumer tip**. No organic food, sold under any recognised symbol, is allowed to be irradiated. According to a survey by the Food Irradiation Campaign in December 1990, virtually all major retailers will not stock irradiated food. However, it is likely to be widely used in the catering trade. Shops not wanting to stock irradiated food sometimes announce their intention by displaying a sticker like the one shown below.

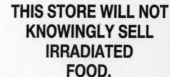

The Radura symbol – being promoted as the international symbol for irradiated food

Poster displayed by stores with a commitment not to sell irradiated food

PURE POISON – FOOD POISONING IN BRITAIN TODAY

The end of the 1980s were a bad time for the food industry in Britain. In particular, 1989 was blessed or cursed with a quite unprecedented series of food scandals, resulting in the resignation of an agriculture minister, the introduction of emergency legislation, bans on the import of selected British foodstuffs by many other European countries, and a huge fall in public confidence in the quality of British food.

We have already looked at some of the issues that came to prominence over this period – pesticide residues in food, the dangers of certain additives and the uproar over plans to irradiate food. But the issue that stayed in the headlines was a mounting fear that British food was contaminated with a whole range of different toxins, bacteria and viruses. Potential food poisoning attacks were apparently lurking in every shopping basket.

Many British people grow up with the prejudice that our food is far cleaner and more hygienic than that of most other countries. Holiday tummy has always been put down to the 'dirty' habits of whatever place people happen to visit on holiday (in fact it is far more likely to be caused by too much alcohol, food and hot sun). So it has come as rather a shock to learn that, in many ways, Britain is lagging behind the rest of Europe. Now that the dust has settled a little, we can identify four main issues.

Slaughterhouses

First, was a series of revelations about conditions in a number of British slaughterhouses. Britain has about 1,000 abbatoirs, and by some estimates less than 100 of these meet European Community standards. The main difference is that in Europe all animals have to be inspected by a qualified veterinary surgeon before slaughter, to prevent the sale of meat from diseased cattle; this still often isn't the case in Britain (and relates directly to the incidences of BSE as described below). However,

there are other problems, relating to hygiene. A Ministry
of Health inspector was interviewed about conditions in
slaughterhouses by *The Guardian* in 1988:

> There are some really disgusting practices which are
> widespread. Machinery is so infrequently cleaned that
> the fat and grease clinging to it grows mould. Meat
> which falls on the floor is just flung back on hooks again.
> Sloppy slaughtering causes the digestive tract to
> rupture and shit literally spills on the meat.

Of course, many slaughterhouses are far better than the
few worst cases. But the fact that most of our abbatoirs
would not be allowed to operate in the same way on
mainland Europe started giving people cause for concern.

Salmonella

The second issue related to the resurgence of food
poisoning, and in particular the rapid increase in cases of
salmonella. Even Donald Acheson, the Chief Medical
Officer at the Department of Health, described this as an
'epidemic'.

Salmonella has been around for a long time. It is one of
the commonest causes of an upset tummy in food
poisoning cases, and is usually traced back to eggs. The
problem stems from the twin facts that cases of salmonella
poisoning are increasing fast and that they are coming
mainly from one particular *Salmonella* bacteria species
that has not been so common before. What this means is
that there is a real increase in both the number and the
severity of the cases. The whole issue became somewhat of
a *cause célèbre* at the beginning of 1989, after a handful of
newspaper exposés. An off the cuff remark by a junior
minister of health, Edwina Currie, about how widespread
the contamination was, caused such an uproar amongst
egg producers that she was forced to resign (such is the
power of the agriculture lobby in British politics).

The interesting thing from our point of view is that the
main new cause of salmonella seems to be the habit of
feeding bits of dead poultry carcasses back to chickens in

33

battery cages, a bizarre form of recycling that has become increasingly popular in recent years. Because there is nothing to force manufacturers of animal feeds to state precisely what is in their feeds, many farmers are unwittingly feeding their chickens on other chickens. The problem is that the chicken carcass remains in the feed may be contaminated with salmonella, providing a source of infection for any chickens that consume the feed. This gives the salmonella bacteria an unrivalled opportunity to spread, and is thought to be the basis of the current increase in infection rates. The government's response has not been to insist that all feed be labelled, or ban the practice of forced cannibalism, but to impose draconian laws regarding testing of flocks, with the subsequent cost to be borne by the producer. While this cost is economically insignificant for large owners of battery units, it is far too expensive for people keeping a small flock, and any of the traditional and free range flocks are being driven out of business. (We return to this subject on page 37.)

Although the incidence of salmonella poisoning is increasing fast, it is still a problem that we have known about for a long time, and which doctors are experienced in dealing with. The next food scares came from the emergence of problems that were either completely new or newly recognised.

Listeria

Listeria is another bacterial form of food poisoning. It is a lot more difficult to contract than salmonella and other more common tummy bugs, but is more serious if you do get infected. Although it has been known about for 50 years or more, listeria has only become important in the last few years because of its ability to survive, and thrive, in refrigerators.

Three types of people are at risk if they get infected – the elderly, people who are already ill and pregnant women. If these classes of people become infected, listeria can be highly dangerous and can cause quite a high

proportion of deaths; statistics suggest that roughly a third
of infected people are likely to die. In the case of pregnant
women, there is a high risk that their children will be
either stillborn or so weak that they die soon after birth.

We seem to have increased the risks of listeria
dramatically by some aspects of modern food processing.
Foods stored in refrigerated conditions, including
pre-prepared salads with dressing, soft cheeses and, most
notoriously, cook-chill foods, are all likely sources of
infection. And contamination rates can be quite high;
estimates for the proportion of salads and cheeses
containing the *Listeria* bacteria are around 10 per cent,
and cook-chill foods are sometimes estimated as having
much higher rates of contamination. This means that
although most of us won't be infected, people at risk, and
especially expectant mothers, should avoid the foods most
likely to contain the bacteria.

BSE, the mad cow disease

The worst is yet to come. The last form of food infection
that we will look at here is also the most contentious. BSE,
or bovine spongiform encephalopathy to give it its full
name, is a new disease of cattle; it is thought to be a
mutated form of the brain disease of sheep called scrapie
that has been around for years, and which causes a fatal
condition called the staggers. It appears that the infective
agent has passed between sheep and cattle because many
cows in intensive farming units are fed on concentrates
that contain, amongst other things, the brains of sheep.
BSE has spread fast through British cattle, and new cases
are appearing all the time; however it is extremely difficult
to tell precisely how fast the problem will increase, as we
don't know how to detect infection before it becomes
obvious, and gestation can take up to 10 years.

BSE has become an issue of international importance
because of fears that it may also pass across to humans.
There is no proof that this can happen as yet, but the
evidence that we do have is far from reassuring. Scientists
have shown that BSE can pass to many other animals,

including cats and pigs. Humans already suffer from a similar disease, called Creuzfeld-Jacob disease, which is invariably fatal. We have, until very recently, been able to eat cow's brains ourselves, as part of the offal that turns up in sausages, beefburgers, pasties and other forms of reconstituted meat; and in any case, we have no way of knowing whether meat from other parts of the animal is not infected as well.

Other countries have reacted to the BSE scare a lot more seriously than our own government, and several have banned imports of British beef as a result. However, they may well be bolting the door long after the horse has fled; British-based feed concentrates, containing sheeps' brains, have been sold on the mainland of Europe for years, so it is likely that BSE has already found its way into other European countries, and will become obvious after the gestation period has elapsed.

What to do?

The key issue in many aspects of food poisoning is the ways in which farm animals are fed. The concentrates that make up animal feeds bear little resemblance to the type of food farm animals would eat in nature. Concentrates can contain a whole ragbag of material, including animal remains – blood, bone, offal and even manure; as we have seen, bits of chicken are ground up, disguised as pellets, and fed to chickens again. Vegetarian, herbivorous animals such as cattle and sheep also get fed animal products. This would be bad enough from an ethical viewpoint, but it is also a highly unhealthy process that risks all kinds of infections, for although the reconstituted concentrates are supposed to be thoroughly sterilised, they are widely acknowledged as being a major cause of the spread of both salmonella and BSE.

The Soil Association launched a new campaign to tighten up regulations regarding animals feeds at the end of 1990. It included a Charter on Animal Feeds, which included the following:

- That animal feeds have all the ingredients listed on the label so that farmers can choose what they feed to their livestock.
- Banning hazardous additives from animals feeds, including dyes, hormones and unnecessary medication.
- Banning the use of animal remains and manures in any animal feeds.

The Soil Association standards provide a model of good practice towards animal feeds; animals are fed 70–90 per cent organic food, and the rest must not contain any animal byproducts.

- **Consumer tips**. If you are seriously worried about BSE, either avoid beef altogether or, at least, avoid the type of reconstituted beef that is made up from a whole range of waste products from the animals. This includes any but the best quality, or organic, sausages, burgers and mince. We still do not know if BSE can be passed from animals to humans.

REFINED TO DEATH

So far we have looked at various forms of food adulteration, both from accidental contamination by pollutants and the deliberate use of additives. But it is not only things that are added to the food that cause the problems; modern methods of food processing also take away some vital ingredients as well. Much of the food we buy today is chronically over-processed. Years of attempting to manufacture refined smooth foods have resulted in a diet that is deficient in roughage, minerals and many vitamins, and high in fats and sugars.

Take roughage for example. Most people with the slightest interest in food and diet now probably know that many modern diets in the west are low in roughage. The classic example is white bread; once the husks of the wheat have been removed the bread loses almost all its fibre. The immediate result is that something like half the people in Britain suffer the discomfort of occasional or chronic constipation. Longer term, the effects of this can increase the risk of haemerrhoids, ulcers, a number of bowel complaints and cancer of the colon. The recommendation of the government's National Advisory Committee on Nutrition Education report is that we should eat, on average, half as much fibre again per day. Other experts think that this still doesn't go far enough.

Realisation of this has caused some changes in our eating patterns. Sales of brown bread have increased, for example, although some of the 'brown' bread sold today is actually made from white flour with brown dye added. Other people resort to bran, which may help do the trick, but means that you are paying out twice, for white bread and bran, whereas you can easily get both in a single loaf of wholemeal bread. Other good sources of fibre include fresh fruit and vegetables, especially if they are eaten raw.

But other food over-refinements are less well known. Some forms of processing, over-cooking and dietary imbalance can lead to deficiencies in certain vitamins and minerals. Others concentrate the amount of fats in foods; for example many reconstituted meat products contain high proportions of fat.

The ways that animals are reared and kept also has an effect on the meat they produce. It is now known that animals that are kept inside, and fed concentrates, are not only fatter than those that are free range, or wild, but the fat tends to contain a far higher proportion of saturated fats, which are widely believed to be more dangerous to health, increasing the risk of heart disease.

Another over-refinement issue that has involved the Soil Association over the last few years is the pasteurisation of milk. The government has made several attempts to ban the sales of unpasteurised green-top milk in Britain. Although pasteurisation was brought in to sterilise milk against a range of bacteria, including especially tuberculosis, many people believe that the process reduces the food value of the milk, and is not a particularly good way of sterilising the milk either.

CAUGHT WITH OUR GENES DOWN

Ever since biologists learned about the secret of the genetic code that governs inheritance and, even more importantly, learned how to swap pieces of genetic material around between different species, the potential of genetic engineering has been fascinating the food industry.

In fact, farmers have practised simple genetic engineering since the dawn of history. Crop and livestock breeding to improve productivity, to increase resistance to disease, to fit species for particular climates, and so on, has always been an important part of agriculture. But as we have learned more about the processes of inheritance, agricultural breeding has become increasingly sophisticated; and the industry is anxious to promote genetic engineering, the splicing of one gene on to another, as simply another step in this process. But this is making a serious under-estimate of the potential of modern genetic engineering.

In the early halcyon days of biotechnology, sober industry analysts started talking like science fiction writers, predicting the imminent arrival of giant tomatoes, grown square for ease of packaging; massively productive livestock; wheat capable of catching its nutrients from the atmosphere; and instant cures for all kinds of diseases. Biotechnologists still talk like this sometimes, but not quite so loudly. The reality of genetic manipulation has proved more difficult to get right, and the medium term goals for agriculture have become more prosaic. However, they are real enough to cause a great deal of concern to people worried about the environmental and ethical aspects of farming.

The most famous, or infamous, example of biotechnology is bovine somatotropin, or BST, an artificial hormone extracted from a genetically manipulated organism and fed to cattle. BST is supposed to increase milk yield by up to 30 per cent, although some tests suggest that the real increase is far smaller. The chemical industry is promoting BST extremely hard at the moment, but has met with unexpected opposition from consumer groups, environmentalists and farmers. This is because a number of problems have emerged. BST certainly puts cattle under greater stress, if only because they have to produce more milk. However, concerned scientists have been arguing for some time that there are a number of other possible side effects on animals as well; this has been vigorously denied by the industry, but after further tests BST has been rejected by the Veterinary Advisory Committee of the British government, and its further use suspended. (BST has already been used in test circumstances, and the milk sold unlabelled in Britain, thereby breaking a voluntary global ban on the release of genetically engineered organisms.) There have also been a number of fears about its impact on human health.

There are a number of other biotechnology issues around at present. Porcine somatotropin (PST) is an equivalent hormone for pigs, which increases weight gain at the expense of the animal's welfare. Several chemical companies are now developing crop strains that are resistant to pesticides so that greater concentrations of pesticides can be sprayed around them as they grow; this is clearly for the benefit of the chemical company that sells the pesticide, rather than the farmer who would prefer a strain that was resistant to the pest.

There are many fundamental ethical and practical questions to answer about the future uses of biotechnology. The problem is that the industrial juggernaut already has a fair bit of momentum as regards genetic engineering, and any attempts at criticism are being met with a barrage of denials by the public relations departments of the agrochemical giants. They see biotechnology as a way forward if the agrochemical industry collapses; but rather than any rational development for the overall human good, the processes are being used in the interests of the agribusiness industry.

The implications for organic farming are complex and serious. Biotechnology companies are busily pushing their wares, and claiming that they will help make organic agriculture easier and more efficient. But many organic farmers think that genetic engineering of this kind is fundamentally opposed to the principles that led Lady Eve Balfour and her colleagues to form the Soil Association in the first place. At the moment, the genetically manipulated products, such as BST and PST, hovering on the edge of the market are clearly unacceptable to organic growers, as they are to the majority of chemical farmers as well. But as genetic engineering becomes more sophisticated and, for example, is used to confer resistance to specific diseases or to maximise nutrient gains, then the questions will become much more complicated.

CONCLUSIONS

This brief overview has introduced some of the most urgent food problems that concern the Soil Association and its members at the present. The fact that these problems have received a lot of attention should not make anyone complacent that the issues will now be properly addressed and solved. Experience suggests that the food industry, given half a chance, will do a little bit of cosmetic re-arrangement and carry on much as before.

The rush to introduce new and dangerous technologies, such as irradiation, BST and other technical fixes, shows that the public enthusiasm for fresh, wholesome food isn't shared by most of the industry that sells food. This shouldn't come as any surprise. Most of the food processing that takes place today has been introduced because it maximises profit rather than anything else. (There may be some exceptions, but the principle remains the same.) Forcing the industry to accept limitations on its growth will not be easy. But, as less and less people buy over-processed additive-ridden and contaminated food, then market-led changes will inevitably occur.

3
WHERE HAVE ALL THE FLOWERS GONE?

Modern food production has not just contaminated our food. It has caused enormous damage to the environment as well, including huge wildlife losses and the large scale degradation of the British countryside. It has become fashionable to blame the farmers for these problems, but, while there certainly are a minority of farmers who put profit before environment, the large majority take a pride in the land they work and want to see it maintained in good health for future generations. Since the Second World War farmers, like most other people, have been led down the path of intensive agriculture by successive governments and by industry. And although the whole philosophy of intensive agriculture is now being challenged, and fundamental changes are being planned, the legacy of this error will be seen on the face of the British countryside for many years to come. Below we look at some of the main problems facing the countryside today.

THE DISAPPEARING LANDSCAPE

One of the most obvious changes since the early decades of this century has been in the rural landscape. The trend towards bigger, more specialised and increasingly mechanised farms has meant the development of larger fields, fewer woods and hedgerows, the ploughing up of ancient pasture and the destruction of many wetlands and heaths.

The rate and extent of this destruction has been enormous. Since 1945, for example, an estimated 97 per cent of ancient, species-rich meadows have been ploughed up, reseeded and treated with fertiliser, or entirely replaced by arable crops. These meadows were enormously rich sources of wildflowers, insects and birds; the number of these species surviving on a monoculture of introduced pasture grass, heavily treated with agrochemicals, is a tiny fraction of the original. Over the same period, more than half our ancient woodlands have been felled. In many cases they have been replaced with plantations of conifers, arranged in uniform rows and planted so densely that the sun cannot penetrate. These do little to provide wildlife habitat once they are fully grown, and they also cause soil erosion and help acidify the soil and water by collecting pollutants from the air that are washed down by rain.

Perhaps the most immediately obvious loss since the Second World War has been the hedgerows, grubbed out to make way for the huge agricultural machines designed to work huge fields. The length of hedgerow destroyed in Britain over this period would stretch seven times around the equator. And even those hedges that do remain are often in a poor state, not properly maintained and continually battered by spray drift from pesticides, so that all but the most hardy bush and flower species disappear. Those hedgerows alongside roads receive additional contamination from lead and other vehicle pollutants, while many local authorities treat verges with pesticides as well, or cut them back at the wrong time of year so that birds' nests are destroyed and flowering plants not given a chance to set seed.

More specialised habitats have suffered as well, under the constant encouragement to plough up more and more land to produce food. In Lancashire the area of bog and marsh has been reduced by 99 per cent since 1865, to make way for more arable land. The area of Dorset heathland has declined by half since 1960. An increasing number of archaeological sites and ancient building remains are being ploughed up or destroyed to make way for new developments.

The existence of laws to protect the countryside are to be welcomed, but unfortunately they are often little more than paper declarations. The rate of destruction of sites of special scientific interest (SSSIs), which are supposed to be protected from interference by law, has been running at 4 per cent per year; this means that about 100 identified sites of scientific and natural history value are being irreparably damaged every year.

Despite the recent upsurge of interest in green issues, the rate of environmental and landscape destruction is continuing to accelerate. A detailed study carried out between 1978 and 1984 found that over this period:

- 28,000 kilometres of hedgerow were removed.
- 39,000 hectares of new housing were built, mainly on farmland.
- 5,000 kilometres of new tracks were laid over upland Britain.

Current plans for the countryside will continue this spiral of destruction. The government intends to introduce a vast new road building scheme, cutting across national parks and hitherto untouched rural areas. New rail links are being constructed to meet the Channel Tunnel. A general relaxation of planning controls is encouraging more building on green-field sites. And a huge increase in conifer plantation is being promoted in the remaining wilderness areas of Scotland and Wales.

Some of these changes are probably inevitable. People have to live and work in the countryside, and this is not always compatible with the most beautiful landscape features. But the scale of destruction has been unprecedented. It has been fuelled, at the heart, by the underlying philosophy of intensive chemically-based agriculture that is now being strongly challenged by organisations such as the Soil Association.

One way in which the Association has responded has been the Crisis in the Countryside campaign, which focused attention not only on the conservation and wildlife problems that could occur through farming methods, but also on the positive role that farmers could adopt to prevent these problems. These issues are described in more detail on pages 77 and 91.

WILDLIFE IN DANGER

Whenever natural or semi-natural habitats disappear, the wildlife suffers as well. In addition, there is a range of new or intensified threats to wild plants and animals as a result of the growth of chemical agriculture. Despite well over a million British people belonging to conservation organisations, there has been a rapid decline in wildlife throughout the country. Key species and habitats continue to decline in the 1990s.

Loss of habitat is certainly the single most important cause. Drainage of wetlands has contributed to the extinction of four out of 41 species of dragonflies since the 1950s. Many other insect species have suffered catastrophic losses – for example, nine out of 26 species of bumble bees have seriously declined in southern England over recent years. Almost 20 heathland plants are at serious risk of becoming extinct in Britain, and many more are surviving in a few remnant populations; even larger numbers of wetland plant species are likely to disappear completely over the next few years unless urgent steps are taken to protect them.

However, it is not only habitat destruction that is to blame. Pesticide poisoning is now known to have played a major role in the decline of many species in the past, and continues, albeit in a more subtle way, to kill huge numbers of wild plants and animals today. Early pesticides were particularly dangerous. Small animals that ate crops that had been treated with pesticides often accumulated these pesticide residues in their bodies. Predators thus received a dose of pesticide residue with each small animal they consumed and, as predators tend to eat a lot of small animals, these species at the top of the food chain received an accumulated dose that was

45

considerable. Several birds of prey, for example, were almost wiped out as a result. Common consequences of this accumulated poisoning were loss of the ability to reproduce successfully, either because the birds became sterile or because eggshells were unnaturally thin and broke before the young bird was developed enough to survive. Particularly susceptible species included peregrines, sparrowhawks and merlins, but many other top predators suffered as well, including the rare golden eagle. In Norfolk, for example, over a period of about 20 years, the number of sparrowhawks fell from 400–500 pairs down to just two breeding pairs.

Today, some of the most persistent organochlorine pesticides have been banned in Britain, although one of the most infamous, DDT, was only finally withdrawn in 1984. However, illegal supplies have remained on sale until recently, and are almost certainly still available to anyone persistent enough to go looking for them. For example, in 1985 a colony of herons were wiped out on the River Avon near Evesham; analysts at the Nature Conservancy Council found the highest levels of DDT, and other persistent pesticides, that they had ever found in wild animals, even though most of these pesticides were already banned in Britain. Evesham is in an area that has suffered heavily from pesticide abuse, including many spray drift incidents.

Other problems still remain. Many birds are killed by deliberate poison baiting, often by gamekeepers. A number of the mid-Wales population of red kites have been killed in this way in recent years; the entire British population is only about 50 pairs at most, and these have only been built up by years of effort by the Royal Society for the Protection of Birds. Large numbers of geese have been killed by accidentally eating seeds treated with toxic pesticides. Otters and other aquatic life have been poisoned by seepage of the particularly hazardous chemicals used in sheep dips, this being a major cause of the decline in otter populations in upland areas of Wales and the Lake District.

But wildlife doesn't just suffer from intense immediate poisoning: the effects of pesticides can also be more subtle. For example, a survey by the Game Conservancy in Hampshire showed that survival of partridge chicks was increased three times in fields where farmers did not spray right up to the hedgerow. Further research showed that the chicks were at risk of starvation; the pesticides that were sprayed right up to the hedgerows killed the wildflower species that were the food of specific insects, which in turn were the food of the partridge chicks. This is borne out by several studies of birds on organic, as compared with chemical, farms, which show that there are consistently higher and more varied bird populations on organic farms.

Wildlife gets a further battering from other sources. Air and water pollution kill or weaken many species, some of the effects being described in the sections below. Until recently the practice of straw burning has killed many small insects and mammals every year; the ban on this burning has yet to come fully into effect. Toxic wastes and other rubbish poison some areas and cover others so that the habitat is destroyed.

DIRTY RIVERS

In 1986 the government's report on *River Water Quality in England and Wales* reported a decline in the number of miles of 'good' quality rivers. This setback was significant in two ways. It was the first time for many years that river water had, on average, got worse rather than better. And it was also the first time that agricultural practices were identified so specifically as being a major part of the problem – virtually all the water boards (now privatised) identified agricultural pollution as being the main cause of the decline. The North West Water Authority wrote that 'Over half the length of river stretches which deteriorated in quality are on account of agricultural drainage both from diffuse and discrete sources', while Severn Trent reported 'Of particular concern is the impact of repeated pollution incidents in rural areas. Silage liquors and animal wastes are so polluting that even small quantities can be sufficient to affect water quality. Repeated minor entries of such wastes are having a chronic effect upon water quality.' And so on.

The news is even worse when you realise that the government's survey did not cover all the pollutants. Two prime problems, nitrate and pesticides, are examined under a different department, and were not taken into account in the survey.

So what are the main agricultural pollutants? We have already looked at the impact of high nitrate levels in the diet (page 18). Nitrate also causes problems to freshwaters (and to the seas around our coasts) when it leaches off fields after fertiliser application or heavy ploughing. Nitrate combines with phosphate to cause eutrophication in ponds and rivers, a process whereby oxygen is used up in water because of excessive plant growth due to oversupply of nutrients. Eutrophication usually involves the rapid growth of algae following a sudden enrichment with nutrients; an algal bloom results, which turns the water a thick soupy green, or the whole area is clogged with a dense mat of filamentous algae. This in turn shades out light from reaching the bottom, so that plants cannot grow properly. More importantly, when the algae die the bacteria that break them down use up all the oxygen, so that other life forms are literally smothered. Nitrate levels continue to rise in many areas, particularly in the heart of the grain growing lands in the south and east of England.

Another important source of nitrate and phosphate is slurry, or liquid manure, from livestock farms. When animals are kept in intensive units, the manure has to be collected and stored in slurry tanks before being used on the land in a managed way, or otherwise disposed of safely. But over the last few years there has been an apparently inexorable rise in the number of incidents in which slurry is released into water. Quite apart from the pathogenic organisms that slurry is likely to contain, the intense burst of nutrients can cause instant problems to freshwaters, including large scale fish kills.

Slurry gets into freshwater either because the slurry tanks burst or leak or, increasingly, because owners deliberately breach the tank in order to get rid of an excess of slurry. The whole problem is intensified because of the large numbers of animals crowded into a small space in a factory farming unit, and the fines for illegal dumping are low enough so that some people are not deterred. And in addition to slurry, modern farms are likely to contain considerable quantities of silage (fermented grass used as cattle feed) and that, in turn, can get into freshwaters and cause similar problems.

However, the major new water pollution of the 1990s looks set to be contamination with pesticides. Strict new regulations from the European Commission are causing long faces in the British Ministry of Agriculture, Fisheries and Food, because there is no way that most British freshwaters will meet them at the moment.

To be honest, pesticides in freshwater are rather an unknown quantity at the moment. The effects of some are well documented, for example in the case of sheep dip and otters described above; others, including the herbicides atrazine and simazine, which are frequently found at levels exceeding those allowed in the EC, are much less thoroughly studied. However these latter chemicals will soon be much more important politically, because they have been included in the government's proposed 'Red List' of substances that are so hazardous that they should be controlled, even from diffuse sources; this means that their use is effectively likely to be illegal in many areas in the near future.

SOMETHING IN THE AIR – ATMOSPHERIC POLLUTION AND FARMING

Agriculture and air pollution have a two-way relationship; farmers suffer crop losses because of the polluted environment, but at the same time modern farming methods contribute some airborne pollutants of their own.

During the 1980s there was a revolution in our understanding of the seriousness and extent of air pollution in the industrialised world. In particular, the related phenomena of acid rain and tree dieback were recognised by virtually all scientists and politicians. We now know that waters in many areas of Europe and North America have become more acid because of pollution from industry, electricity generation and road transport. The most important acid pollutants are sulphur dioxide and nitrogen oxides. These major sources of air pollution have also been responsible for, or at the very least a major contributory factor in, the widespread forest decline, or *Waldsterben*, that is causing such devastation throughout the northern latitudes.

However, air pollution has other effects as well. Acid rain is eroding many old buildings and monuments, and is turning the soil itself acid. Air pollution is beginning to destroy native species of plants and animals; susceptible plant groups include many lichens and mosses, club mosses and, it is increasingly realised, flowering plants as well, while amongst animals, molluscs, some amphibians and certain water-feeding birds, including the stream-living dipper, are being affected. And a range of airborne pollutants, including ozone, hydrocarbons and lead, are recognised as being damaging to human health. In addition, recent research also suggests that air pollution is almost certainly damaging crops, and may well be significantly reducing yields.

It has taken a long time to reach this last conclusion. Crop scientists have been looking at the effects of various air pollutants on plants for many years, and the consensus has, until recently, been that the levels of pollutants such as sulphur dioxide and nitrogen oxides found in the air were far too low to cause any significant damage to crops. But two things helped change the researchers' minds.

First, it has been shown that mixtures of two or more pollutants are, in some cases, more toxic than the sum of their individual effects. This effect, known as synergism or the cocktail effect, means that all the laboratory studies into the impact of individual pollutants on crops have very little relevance to real life; instead, plant physiologists have to look at the impact of the mixture of pollutants that is actually present in the air.

Secondly, the levels of ozone in the air were found to be much higher than anyone had suspected. Ozone is known to be toxic to crop plants on its own, and it also acts synergistically with other pollutants. Suddenly botanists were faced with a much less comforting picture of the state of Britain's agricultural crops. It is now accepted that some reductions in crop growth are probably occurring, and susceptible species may well be weakened in other ways, perhaps by becoming less resistant to disease. Figures of losses are little more than guesstimates at the moment, although overall losses of around 5 per cent of the total have been suggested. It must certainly vary enormously between species, between different areas of the country, between different times of the year, and from one year to the next, so any precise measurements will remain impossible.

There may be other problems as well. In the last few years it has been shown that acid rain also acidifies soils in some areas, especially where they are already slightly acid to start with and thus unable to neutralise extra acid material from air pollution. This may well lead to other phenomena, including the release of toxic materials into the soil such as aluminium and heavy metals. We don't know what effects this could have on grazing animals or on crops. What we do know, fairly definitely, is that a lot of farmers are suffering economic losses because of the damage caused by industrial pollution.

On the other hand, the farmers are making their own contribution to the general pollution load. The most important agricultural air pollutants are pesticides, and these enter the air in a number of ways. The most frequent occurrence is when pesticide is sprayed on to a field and some of the droplets drift away in the wind; this is known as spray drift or drop drift. In addition, some pesticides can evaporate after landing on crops or the soil, sometimes as long as three days after being applied, and this vapour drift can also be important in some places. (There have been moves to withdraw some of the most volatile herbicides that are liable to vapour drift.) Lastly, pesticide applied as dusts or granules can also be spread by winds. All these phenomena are usually lumped together under the one term of spray drift.

Pesticide spray can obviously have immediate effects if it lands on neighbouring crops, blows into hedges or drifts across roads or gardens. We have already seen how drift can damage wildlife around the margins of fields (see page 47), but spray drift damage to crops can also be a serious problem; weedkillers from grain fields can drift on to vegetable patches and cause havoc, this being particularly common where arable crops are grown next to market garden vegetables, such as in the Vale of Evesham or in parts of Lincolnshire. There have also been a number of well documented cases where people have suffered minor or serious health effects because they were caught in pesticide drift.

However, spray drift may have longer term effects as well. Although pesticides have become chemically more sophisticated over the years, the equipment used to apply them has not changed to the same degree. One of the results is that the spray is released in droplets of many different sizes. Some comes out in very large drops, which usually bounce straight off the plant and are lost to the soil. But other drops are extremely small; up to a fifth of the spray can emerge as droplets of under 100 microns in diameter (a micron is a thousandth of a millimetre). At this size the drops are so light that they are likely to drift, whatever the weather conditions, and to stay in the air almost indefinitely. If water is used as the dilutant, this will eventually evaporate, leaving a particle of pure chemical. There has never been any research carried out into the health and environmental effects of the steady chronic pollution of the air with such tiny droplets of a whole range of air pollutants.

Farming can cause other problems as well. The slurry from factory farm units, which we have already discussed because of its impact on water pollution (see page 17), can also release substantial quantities of ammonia to the atmosphere. The Netherlands has identified this as one of the most important air pollutants in places where there are a lot of factory farms, and Dutch scientists have linked it with *Waldsterben*. Air pollution from slurry is now also thought to be a potential problem in parts of Britain, including East Anglia.

Indeed, the more scientists look at intensive farming, the more pollution problems seem to emerge. Over the past couple of years, factory farming units have also been linked to the production of methane, which is an important factor in global warming, this methane resulting both from the slurry units and from flatulence in cattle, now admitted to be a problem of global proportions. This issue is discussed in more detail on page 68.

LOSING GROUND – SOIL EROSION IN BRITAIN

We have already discussed the role of soil erosion in the 1930s and 1940s in stimulating the initial environmental interest that led to the formation of the Soil Association. Many people probably think that these problems are now a thing of the past: unfortunately, they are not. Research carried out by the Soil Association has shown that soil erosion is alive and well in Britain, and is increasingly being seen as a serious problem by conventional agricultural planners and scientists.

In fact the problem of soil erosion resulting from intensive farming practices has been recognised for some time. The Strutt Report (a report of the Agricultural Advisory Committee) in the 1970s drew attention to the dangers, and specifically charged intensive farming with making the problem worse; more recent research, especially on the South Downs and in Bedfordshire, has drawn attention to the fact that erosion has continued to increase rapidly since then. Surveys conclude that at least

44 per cent of our agricultural soils are now at risk of serious losses.

Some erosion is expected, and natural, and farmland has the ability to create more soil from underlying bedrock, from humus and from other material. The problems arise, when soil is eroded so fast that it cannot be replaced. Research suggests that in bad years in Britain soil losses can reach 40 tonnes per hectare per year, and spectacular losses of up to 100 or 200 tonnes per hectare per year are by no means unknown. This is less than in certain tropical areas where monsoon rains occur, but it is high enough to cause very serious problems within parts of Britain. A number of specific causes have been identified, and linked with intensive farming techniques. These include:

- Having the land under continuous arable cultivation.
- Converting larger areas of grassland to arable crops.
- Increasing the area of land under cereals.
- Using heavy machinery, which damages soil structure.
- Creating 'tramlines' or machinery tracks of bare soil in a growing crop.
- Working the land up and down a slope, instead of across the slope, and increasing cultivation on steep upland slopes.
- Removing hedges, copses and other windbreaks.
- Cultivating at times of the year when erosion is likely, i.e. by leaving land bare over winter, when erosion is likely through the action of rain and snow, or ploughing in very dry periods when wind erosion is a problem.
- The production of fine seed beds, particularly in relation to winter cereal crops.

In 1987 the Soil Association launched a national programme, Soilwatch, to monitor soil erosion. It has also been active in promoting the use of organic methods in reducing soil erosion, and the potential of this is now widely recognised, as described on page 88.

4
PRISONERS OF CONSCIENCE – ANIMALS AND AGRICULTURE

'They often exercise their wings by stretching one leg and the wing on the same side of the body at the same time in a backwards direction. This movement requires considerably less space than wing flapping.' And this, according to the experts at the Ministry of Agriculture, Fisheries and Food, means that keeping four chickens in a cage measuring 16 by 18 inches is quite acceptable from a welfare point of view.

The treatment of farm animals in intensive livestock units (a more acceptable phrase to the industry than 'factory farms') is one of the moral issues that most of us simply try to ignore. Almost everyone is aware that a lot of farm animals lead miserable unnatural lives. Many people also know that they are fed unnatural food, are not allowed access to their young, and are mutilated and drugged. The traditional picture of farm animals walking about happily in fields or barns is still the one presented to the public; however, in many cases it is now totally untrue.

But what can you do about it? About a million people in Britain have rejected meat altogether, and the number of such vegetarians is rising all the time. Many other people don't like what they hear about the treatment of farm animals, but do like meat. So most of us just carry on buying our steaks and sausages and try to close our eyes to what is happening.

In 1989 the Soil Association launched its Campaign for

Safe Meat, and it proved to be one of the most contentious things the organisation had done for years. The campaign was launched with an investigation into all aspects of meat production, including treatment of animals, hygiene, environmental effects and global issues (we look at many of these aspects in other parts of this book).

The Soil Association's campaign was out of the ordinary in two ways. It was the first time that anyone had looked at all aspects of meat production, ranging from the destruction of tropical rainforests to make hamburgers (see page 65) to the use of veal crates. It was also the first time that an organisation had done a detailed critique of the meat industry from the perspective of the meat eater. The Association was not necessarily saying 'give up meat' but 'give up meat from animals kept in unacceptable ways'. And this was what made the industry so upset.

The campaign sparked off a wave of indignation. Farming organisations were angry because they felt that all people keeping livestock had been tarred with the same brush, and pointed out that many farmers still kept their animals in extensive ways, and cared a great deal about their health and welfare (we certainly wouldn't dispute this). Retailers didn't like the campaign because it threatened their business. Some vegetarian members of the Soil Association resigned because they felt the organisation was going too far in promoting meat eating.

None the less, what the campaign did manage to do was put the meat issue firmly back on the agenda, and lay down the groundwork for developing safer and better alternatives. It also helped create the growing market in organic meat. Some of the issues tackled by the campaign, particularly relating to welfare, are summarised in this chapter.

LIVING CONDITIONS

In natural conditions, animals will live outside; eat natural food; seek out shelter for the night and during bad weather; court, mate and raise their young; and, in the fullness of time, they will fall sick and die, or be killed by accident or a predator. Life is neither comfortable nor particularly long for most wild animals, and there is little to be gained in romanticising their existence. Neither should we mythologise the life of farm animals in the past, which would often live fairly poor lives and be slaughtered messily and with considerable suffering. However, our treatment of farm animals has reached new depths of cruelty with the conditions in the worst factory farm units.

First of all, animals are denied access to open air, natural pasture or even adequate room to move for long periods – in many cases for virtually their whole lives. Factory farmed poultry, which make up the vast majority of egg-laying birds in Britain, usually have about 8 inches (20 cm) square to move around in; yet their average wingspan is 30 inches (75 cm). This means that they can never even stretch their wings properly, let alone walk about. It is by no means unusual to find 20,000 birds in one windowless shed, where the lights are kept on for 17 hours a day to maximise egg laying. Cage floors are of wire mesh to allow droppings to fall straight through, but are uncomfortable for the birds.

Broiler chickens, i.e. those reared for meat, are kept in huge broiler sheds where they roam freely over the floor. Although this is at least partially acceptable when the birds are young, as they reach full size (after only about seven weeks, due to the combination of drugs and concentrates they are fed) they are so crowded that they can hardly move. Again, bright lights are kept burning for much of this period so that feeding (and hence fattening) is maximised. Turkeys are also raised in broiler houses, usually with about 5,000 birds to a unit.

Pictures of conditions in factory farming units have so disgusted consumers that there is a large move towards the purchase of free range eggs. However, beware of the label. Chickens Lib, the society that opposes the battery farming system, estimates that at least half the eggs sold as 'free range' actually come from factory farming units, and fraud is obviously being practised on a massive scale.

So what exactly does 'free range' mean? The European Commission definition of 'free range' is not what most people imagine. In many free-range units poultry are kept in large sheds, just as in the broiler system, with occasional access to a tiny outside pen, through an even tinier door. They are certainly not scratching happily around the farmyard. Indeed, keeping hens in a truly free-range system has become increasingly difficult because of the expensive testing options introduced in the wake of the salmonella scare (see page 32), even though the increase in salmonella is due to factory farming rather than the free-range systems. Small producers, keeping chickens in a humane way, have been penalised totally without justification. Your eggs come bearing a high price in terms of ill treatment of the egg layers.

Unlike poultry, there are still quite a lot of pigs kept in relatively free range conditions, although here as well the tendency is for an increase in intensive units, with over half the sows are now being kept in confined conditions. This means that they are kept in tiny stalls where they have room to stand up, lie down and feed, but nothing else. They are frequently tethered, or held in a girdle around their middles, which can lead to sores and further prevents them from moving around. The floor of the unit is concrete, so the sow is unable to rout with her snout, which is the pig's most sensitive organ. Piglets raised for meat are also often confined to intensive units.

Although the British government has now, finally, outlawed the use of the infamous veal crates for raising veal calves, British calves are still exported to Europe, where the veal crate is in constant operation. The amount of time that beef and dairy cattle stay indoors is also increasing, although we have yet to see the massive concrete feedlots that confine cattle in tiny areas in many parts of the United States. As it is, many calves spend their whole lives indoors, without ever seeing pasture or the open air.

REPRODUCTION AND MATERNITY

Apart from imprisoning animals so that they cannot move around, the next major way in which their natural lives are curtailed is in the methods used for breeding. For a start, many animals are not allowed to mate and are subjected to artificial insemination (AI) instead, which in itself can lead to psychological and behavioural problems in cattle, for example. Although AI has never really been accepted by British pig farmers, the mating is often brutalised; in tethered animals even copulation takes place in confinement by means of a so-called 'rape rack'.

Once born, the young animals are usually taken away from the mother as quickly as possible, thus stopping her following through her maternal instincts. Chicks are taken away at birth; piglets are now frequently taken from sows after a couple of weeks; calves may be quickly separated from cows in some production systems. The animals have no family life.

FITTING SQUARE PEGS IN ROUND HOLES

Animals do not just take such mistreatment lying down. They react in ways that are easy to compare with the ways in which we would react ourselves when put into intolerable living conditions (although the comparison is not really accurate). For example, they get stressed and ill; they fight and, being unable to fight the humans that keep them locked up, they fight each other; sometimes they practise cannibalism.

The factory farming fraternity does not tackle these problems by changing conditions, but by trying to change the animals to fit these conditions. Male cattle and pigs are routinely castrated to make them more docile. Chickens go through debeaking to stop them pecking each other, and cockerels are caponised, i.e. castrated. Pigs are often docked (i.e. their tails are removed) because tail biting becomes common in overcrowded conditions. The animals get fed tranquilisers, just as humans do when they get stressed.

The stress and overcrowding also makes animals ill. All intensively farmed animals have constant medication, often added to their food as a matter of course, but this still does not prevent widescale incidence of disease. Pigs are likely to suffer from liver complaints, pneumonia, meningitis and gastro-enteritis, all at far higher levels than in the past. Young chickens suffer from runting syndrome, a relatively new disease, which stops them developing properly. Cattle now face the risk of mad cow disease, or BSE (as described on pages 36–6), which causes them intense suffering. All of which is good news for the drug companies that sell livestock medicines, and the veterinary profession, but not so good for the animals themselves.

INSTITUTIONAL CANNIBALISM

It is not only stress and overcrowding that wrecks the health of factory farmed animals. They get fed rubbish as well. Instead of eating natural food, pecking, grazing or rooting, animals are fed mainly on high concentration pellets so that they can be fattened quickly for the slaughter. These pellets contain anything that is cheap, accessible and likely to maximise productivity. In recent years there has been a great deal of debate about the practice of feeding herbivorous animals with reconstituted remains of other animals – usually any bits that remain after the meat has been sold. Some pellets also contain reconstituted manure, and if you feed an animal shit, what sort of meat can you expect?

This unnatural practice seems to have created some monstrous health problems, including the rapid spread of salmonella (see pages 33–4) and the creation of the entirely new disease of bovine spongiform encephalopathy (see pages 35–6). The major problem, however, is that most farmers have no idea of what they are feeding their animals; there is no obligation on manufacturers to list ingredients on the packet.

TRANSPORT AND SLAUGHTERING

Farm animals do not just suffer on the farm. Their experience in markets, while being transported and, eventually, in the slaughterhouse are all times when potentially they can suffer from brutality, neglect and poor conditions.

Transport is often a particularly stressful period. Animals are packed into lorries, and then often on to cross-channel ferries; they are frightened, cramped, and without adequate (or sometimes any) food and water. Up to 600 lambs, for example, can be packed so tightly into a railway carriage that they cannot lie down, and are transported for 36 hours without food or water before being sold. Apart from the enormous physical suffering involved, these animals are intelligent enough to feel terrified by what is happening; and it is admitted that the stress of journeys often brings on illness in livestock (this fact was used recently in an advertisement by a drug company, suggesting that all sheep should be treated against *Pasteurella haemolytica* before going on a journey, to reduce the chances of an outbreak). The freeing of the trade barriers within Europe in 1992 will increase the transport of animals and, inevitably, will increase their stress at the same time.

We have already mentioned some of the hygiene problems connected with slaughterhouses on page 33, but this is by no means the only problem. Although for many people the concept of humane slaughter is impossible, the amount of stress that an animal suffers in the process leading up to slaughter can be substantially reduced. However this rarely occurs.

The Soil Association promotes a type of farming that is based on a totally different philosophy of keeping and caring for animals. Some aspects of this are discussed in detail under the section on organic meat on page 80. The debate about vegetarianism and organic farming is to be found on page 100.

5
THE GLOBAL WEB – FARMING, FOOD AND THE WORLD'S ENVIRONMENT

'Ah,' say the supporters of agribusiness, 'it's all very well for a few middle class do-gooders in Britain to worry about the finer points of food quality and environmental destruction. But, what about the vast majority of the people in the world who don't lead such a cosseted existence – the poor in the north and most of the people in the south. Can we afford to worry about tiny amounts of pesticide residues in food when many millions of people still don't have enough to eat? Surely we have to intensify our farming as much as we possibly can, and try to sort out the environmental problems as and when they arise?'

This argument is wrong for a number of reasons. First, it ignores the link between environmental problems and the problems of producing enough food. Second, it ignores the links between politics, with a small p, and the problems of producing enough food. And, lastly, it assumes that intensive agriculture is capable of coming up with the goods in terms of food production, even though on the evidence since the Second World War this patently hasn't been possible so far. This chapter looks at some of the wider issues involved with food and farming.

FEEDING THE 5 BILLION

In a few years time 90 per cent of the world's people will
be found in the continents of Asia, Africa and Latin
America. The rapid growth in the population of third
world countries has led to a lot of rather vague fears about
overpopulation, and has been used as an excuse for the
continued development, and export, of intensive farming
systems. In fact, at the moment there are no good reasons
why anyone should go hungry, and there is more than
enough food produced in the world to feed everyone alive,
and a good many more. And while we're on the subject,
very few third world countries have anything like the
population density of the UK.

The problems of famine, malnutrition and hunger are
much more complex than portrayed by many politicians
and most of the media. They are often linked to
distribution of food, which in turn depends on global issues
such as financial markets and international politics, along
with more local problems like the ability to transport food
efficiently, storage of food, land ownership, and so on. For
example, at the height of the Ethiopian famine in 1985
there were still large quantities of grain being exported
from that country.

None the less, there are certainly good reasons for
improving the efficiency and productivity of agriculture in
many places. And some technological developments are
helping this process, such as some of the improvements in
irrigation technique, the introduction of some of the new
crop varieties, the development of cheap and simple
labour-saving machinery, and improved soil management.

Other developments, though, are making things worse
rather than better. For example, some huge irrigation
schemes simply have not worked, despite the injection of a
great deal of money and 'expertise' from the so-called
developed countries. In dryland areas, irrigation has
resulted in a high concentration of salt reaching the
surface soil, which can then no longer support plants and
consequently reverts to desert. Other large irrigation

63

projects that include the building of artificial lakes upset
the water balance further downstream, so that, while some
farmers benefit, others find it impossible to continue their
cultivation. And this is to ignore the environmental effects.
So, what at first sight seems a beneficial development ends
up doing more harm than good, this being doubly so if a
sustainable traditional way of agriculture is replaced with
a more 'modern' system based on western experience
which fails to deliver the goods.

But environmental problems can occur on a much
larger scale when the entire climate of an area is altered.
This is now happening in places where there has been
large scale deforestation, or where the amount of standing
water has been drastically changed by irrigation or
hydropower schemes.

However, many food problems are also political. Some
of the best intentioned projects undertaken in the third
world have ended up not really helping most of the people
who live in the area. One of the best known examples of
this has been the so-called green revolution, in which
countries like India were supplied with new
higher-yielding strains of crops in the 1960s and 1970s.
Although the crops did, indeed, give higher yields, they
frequently required high doses of artificial pesticides and
fertilisers, and these were only accessible to the richer
farmers, who could then undercut their poorer neighbours
in the marketplace. Poor farmers thus went out of
business, and the land became concentrated in fewer
hands. People started growing food for profit (which
usually meant for export) rather than just for eating or
selling locally. The result of the green revolution in many
countries was that the amount of food in the average diet
actually went down, even though average productivity
went up.

Today political problems still impinge on food
production far more than most of us realise. The debt
crisis is forcing many countries in the third world to
maximise their foreign earnings, and this means planting
more and more cash crops, which in turn takes land out of

production for local food supplies. This pressure on the land is continually increasing. Control and influence by the huge transnational corporations is also balanced in favour of the diets of people in the wealthy north rather than those in the impoverished south.

THE HAMBURGER CONNECTION

Sometimes the links between the food we eat and the environment can seem very obscure at first sight. But this doesn't necessarily mean that they are insignificant.

Take the tropical rainforests for example. Despite the luxurious growth of many tropical forests, the soil underneath is often quite poor, and most of the nutrients are locked into the plants themselves. This works fine so long as the trees remain, but if they are felled or burnt, the soil left behind often cannot sustain agriculture for more than a few years. Some ecologists have described tropical rainforest as being like a jungle growing on a desert.

But the fact that tropical rainforest is not usually suitable for the development of sustainable agriculture hasn't stopped people from trying. Perhaps the most infamous example has been the clearance of huge areas of tropical forest to create rangeland for cattle ranching. Ecologist and film-maker Herbert Giradet describes an apocalyptic scene from Amazonia:

> The savannah country below was on fire. From horizon to horizon columns of smoke were rising thousands of feet into the air. Hills were hardly visible. Wherever we landed on our seven hour flight, grass and small trees were on fire.
>
> I could not believe the scale of what was happening. As we took off again from Conceicao for the last leg of our flight east to Redancao, the smoke became so thick that the pilot lost his way. Some of the passengers had tears running down their cheeks. The acrid smoke, the feeling of helplessness and outrage in the face of so much destruction left us gasping.

65

He brought back extraordinary pictures of cattle wandering through the still-burning remains of a forest. Once cleared, the land is often seeded by aeroplane. Powerful insecticides, including the infamous 2,4,5-T, are sometimes used to destroy any remaining vegetation. This is not farming in any recognised sense.

Already, 100,000 square kilometres of the Brazilian Amazon have been cleared for cattle ranching. The supporters of forest ranching say that they are getting rid of unproductive forest and creating permanent farmland. But they're not. The average lifetime of many Latin American forest ranches is only about five years, after which the land is abandoned to scrub or desert. Even when the farm is operating 'efficiently' (viewed from a very short-term perspective), cattle stocking rates are low and growth is slower than average; the meat tends to be poor and is often used for home consumption, leaving the prime beef raised on the pampas for export.

Hence the title of this section. Although the forest clearance does not usually provide meat directly for export, the fact that all the good land is used for exported, burger meat, means that additional areas have to be cleared to produce poorer quality meat for home consumption. The proportion of meat in the diet of people in some Latin American countries has actually declined in the last few years, despite a huge increase in cattle raising.

Furthermore, the ranches do not replace 'unproductive' forest. They replace a vast and complex ecosystem that has a vital, and increasingly recognised, part to play in maintaining the planet's environment. Burning forest now accounts for about a fifth of all carbon dioxide released into the atmosphere, and carbon dioxide is the most important of the greenhouse gases that are currently changing the world's climate. The loss is even more significant because the tropical forests are also a vital element in absorbing carbon dioxide from the air. So, once lost, they tip the global ecosystem further off balance.

FARMING FOR PROFIT?

Cattle ranching has transformed the environment in many South and Central American countries. Between 1960 and 1990 the amount of pastureland in Costa Rica, for example, increased from an eighth to a third of the whole country, and beef production tripled. But as most of the meat was exported, the average Costa Rican did not benefit, and beef consumption within the country actually declined over the same period. What's worse, much of the new pasture has already been abandoned, for reasons already described.

Of course, people living in tropical forest countries have every right to improve the agricultural land and use their forests. But many of the current developments don't really benefit these countries at all; the profits either go directly to foreign companies owning the land, or are used to help service the massive debts that are crippling the economies of many countries. 'Cheap' imported food isn't necessarily as cheap in real terms as it may appear at first sight.

THE COW AND THE ICECAP – FARMING AND GLOBAL WARMING

Global warming and environment issues are inextricably linked when we start looking at the impact of farming on the world's climate. Much attention has been paid to global warming over the past few years, and the consensus amongst specialists is increasingly that the greenhouse effect is both real and a serious problem.

Much of the sun's heat that reaches the earth's surface is reflected or radiated back outwards again. The layer of greenhouse gases is vitally important in trapping this heat and ensuring that the temperature on the earth's surface is kept at a reasonable level. The problem is that the proportion of these greenhouse gases in the atmosphere is increasing, more of the sun's heat is being trapped and the temperature of the earth's surface is consequently rising. This is thought to be causing freak weather conditions around the world and, in time, will lead to a rise in the temperature of the oceans and a subsequent melting of the polar ice caps. The greenhouse effect is thus threatening world agriculture and could also lead to flooding of huge areas of land and many cities as the sea levels rise. Several international treaties have pledged themselves to tackle this problem, but little action has been taken to date.

Although carbon dioxide, released by burning fossil fuels and wood, is the most important greenhouse gas, it only accounts for about half the global warming potential. The next most important gas is methane, which has doubled in atmospheric concentration over the last 200–300 years, and is currently increasing at a rate of about 1 per cent per year.

Worldwide, agriculture is one of the most important sources of methane, and two of the most important agricultural sources are rice paddies and livestock, especially ruminants such as cows, sheep and buffalo – every year the world's cattle release something of the order of 60 to 100 million tonnes of methane into the atmosphere. It might seem bizarre that flatulence in cattle could become an issue of global concern, that it might be part of a chain that could fundamentally and irrevocably alter the earth's climate and flood vast cities such as London and New York. But the truth of this is now virtually undisputed, and in September 1990 the Intergovernmental Panel on Climate Change produced a whole report on ways of limiting methane production, including strategies for reducing methane emissions from the world's cattle.

FOOD FOR THE 21st CENTURY

As we said in the introduction, this book is by no means all
doom and gloom. The Soil Association's critique of current
farming practice, and of food processing, is firmly rooted
in the knowledge that things don't have to be as bad as
this. Since the Second World War, organic farmers and
gardeners have been developing an alternative farming
strategy. While other people were turning their farms into
intensive chemical-powered food factories, a small band of
organic farmers were quietly researching and refining a
system of producing food that is summarised by the Soil
Association:

> Organic agriculture is an environmentally friendlier way
> of producing high quality, healthy food by crop rotation
> and natural inputs, whilst treating farm animals with
> real concern for their well being. It treats nature as an
> ally not an enemy.

Today, when the shortcomings of intensive agriculture
have become so obvious that they can no longer be
ignored, people involved in the food industry are starting
to take the organic message seriously. So are politicians,
farmers – indeed anyone concerned about what is going
into their shopping basket.

Consumers are reacting against the rash of food scares,
environmental problems and stories about ill-treatment of
livestock by buying ever increasing quantities of organic
food. Opinion polls consistently show that most people in
Britain would prefer to buy organic produce if it was more
widely available, and many say they are prepared to pay
extra for certified organic produce. To be fair, many such
people are still often buying organic food as a reaction – a
protest – against some aspect of mass-produced food,
rather than for the positive aspects of organic food; but as

time goes by, more and more people are choosing it for positive reasons.

However, despite the widespread support, many people still know very little about organic food. If asked, people say it is 'food grown without pesticides' or 'food grown in traditional ways'. Neither of these definitions means much in practice, and they certainly don't define organic farming. This section of the book therefore looks at what organic food really is, how much food we could grow organically, and why we don't already have many more organic farmers in Britain. It summarises what we know about the advantages of organic food. Most important of all, it explains where you can buy it or how you can grow your own organic produce at home.

6
WHAT IS ORGANIC FARMING?

There are a lot of myths about organic agriculture. Many people think it means a return to 'old fashioned farming'. One pesticide company recently described organic farming as the type of farming that was practised at the time of the Irish potato famine! Others think organic methods merely mean leaving out the artificial pesticides and fertilisers, rather than a totally different system of farming. Not many people realise that there are also strict animal welfare standards, or, at least under the Soil Association Standards, an obligation to practise environmental protection.

So what is organic farming? Organic agriculture is an environmentally friendlier alternative to intensive chemically-based production methods, based on an entirely different philosophy of growing crops and raising livestock. It takes as a starting point some traditional methods of maintaining productivity and controlling pests and weeds, and uses these in a more sophisticated way through an understanding of ecology, soil science and crop breeding. It utilises many safe technological developments. Although organic practice is now established, and working, throughout the world, our understanding of the system continues to grow fast, and production methods develop accordingly.

There are a number of characteristics of organic farming:

CROP ROTATIONS

The cornerstone of the organic method is the regular rotation of crops. This serves two functions. It helps to maintain soil fertility, usually by including a *leguminous crop*, i.e. a member of the pea and bean family, which is capable of collecting nitrogen from the air by means of bacteria in the root nodules. The legume crop, along with a phase of the rotation where the land is left fallow, helps maintain the soil fertility without the use of soluble artificial fertilisers. In addition, because different plants have different nutritional requirements, the rotation helps stop the soil becoming imbalanced because of depletion of certain key nutrients, as can happen if the same crop is grown all the time.

Rotating crops also breaks the life cycle of many pests and diseases that are confined to growing on one type of crop; by the time this host crop is planted again, any pests, eggs or spores will usually have died. For example, the cabbage root fly, which is a major pest of any brassica crop, dies during the period of the rotation when there are no members of the cabbage family present. The fact that the same crops are grown in the same field year after year on many modern chemical farms is a major reason why these farmers have to rely so heavily on pesticides to control their pests.

Crop rotations are not fixed, and the farmer or gardener chooses the best rotation for his or her particular needs and locality. One such example of a typical rotation is:

Legumes → Cereal → Pasture → Potatoes

but there are many more.

NON-CHEMICAL PEST AND DISEASE CONTROL

The use of pesticides is avoided if at all possible. Most pesticides kill predators of pests along with the pests themselves; but the latter breed more quickly, so the farmer soon has a bigger problem than before he started. Even if very specific pesticides are made which only kill a particular species, the fact that all members of this species disappear at the same time means that the animals that feed on them also disappear because of lack of food. As we saw earlier (page 47) use of herbicides can also have knock-on effects, by killing wild flowers in hedgerows and depriving beneficial insects of food.

Organic farmers control pests in a variety of ways. The principal method is to encourage a healthy population of natural predators, so that invertebrate pest species are kept in check. Occasionally certain predators will be deliberately introduced, especially into greenhouses where conditions are inevitably less like a natural system. But there are many other pest control strategies, such as planting at a time that avoids the life cycle of a particular pest, the use of barriers and of traps. Plant breeders are having increasing success in developing crop varieties that are resistant to moulds and fungi, thus avoiding the use of fungicides. Weeds are controlled by a variety of methods, including the use of mechanical weeders, the flaming of weeds, covering the ground with mulches to stop weeds appearing, etc. (many of these are described in more detail on a garden scale in chapter 13). In contrast, the practice of most farmers has been to reach for a chemical solution every time a pest occurs and, increasingly, in case a pest appears.

There is still a great deal to be learned about pest control in an organic system. Organic methods require better understanding of individual pests and their lifestyles, and quite a lot of technical development is needed; for example, there has been little work carried out on improving tractor-drawn weeders for use in fields or market gardens. That having been said, conventional farmers are almost always surprised when they go around organic farms when they see that pests and weeds are not necessarily a major problem. Once the system is working properly (and this may take quite a while) the pest problem reduces dramatically.

Of course, there are still occasions when unusual weather conditions, or some other chance factor, results in

a major pest outbreak. At this stage, organic farmers have
recourse to a small range of mainly plant-based pesticides,
including pyrethrum and derris. Like anything designed to
kill pests, these have their risks attached. However, they
have low mammalian toxicity and, crucially, break down
very quickly after use, so that effects are not persistent.
But most organic farmers don't like using pesticides at all,
simply because it breaks down the natural pest control
system which they work hard to achieve.

RECYCLING VALUABLE NUTRIENTS

Not all the necessary nutrients for balanced farming can
come simply from a rotation of plant crops; in most cases,
additional nutrients have to be added. For organic farmers
there are several ways of doing this.

Managed use of manure
Almost all organic farms include animals. Farm animals
graze on fields during the fallow period of the rotation, and
their manure provides accessible nutrients. Manure is also
collected from animals during times when they are kept
inside, although there are strict controls over the ways in
which this is used, so as to prevent leaching and pollution.
Some manure may be mixed with straw and composted.

Making and using compost
The use of compost as a balanced source of nutrients, and
a way of improving soil structure, is probably more
important to organic gardeners and market gardeners
than to farmers, although a few farmers do use large
compost heaps to help recycle nutrients.
  Composting speeds up the process of breakdown in
plant and animal wastes, releasing nutrients so that they
can be taken up by plants again. If done correctly, the
compost gets hot enough in the centre of the heap to kill
many weed seeds, moulds and other diseases. Good
compost also helps build up soil structure and prevents
erosion and soil loss.

Use of selected natural fertilisers

Obviously the farm or garden is not a closed system, because produce is being removed and sold. There are therefore a number of additions to the soil that are permitted in most organic systems, including bonemeal, dried blood, seaweed fertilisers and certain minerals.

The criteria for selection of these natural fertilisers look at both the effects of use on the field, and the impact of manufacture or collection. For example, Chilean nitrate, which comes from the guano of seabirds off the coast of Chile, used to be permitted for organic farmers; however it has been banned both because it increases leaching and its collection causes environmental damage, and it comes from a finite source.

Sewage sludge and composting toilets

In theory, recycling human waste should be an important part of any organic system. The nutrients from the crops pass through our own bodies and currently form a pollution problem, but with proper treatment these could be reused on the fields. However, there are problems of eliminating health risk from any family units such as a composting toilet, and sewage sludge is frequently contaminated with industrial pollutants including heavy metals.

Few organic farmers use nutrients from human waste at the moment in Britain, but we hope that research will allow this to take place more generally in the future.

MAINTAINING A HEALTHY SOIL STRUCTURE

The name Soil Association underlines the key role that the early organic farmers assigned to the health and role of the soil in agriculture. In the most extreme of the chemical farms, soil becomes little more than a medium for holding crops and liquid chemicals, rather like a hydroponics system.

Looking after the soil therefore does not just mean that it must have enough variety of nutrients for the plants to grow. The soil must have a healthy structure, to reduce erosion, and should also have a vigorous community of soil life to make sure that the available nutrients are recycled as quickly as possible, and to allow natural predators to help control outbreaks of pests and pathogens. The use of the rotation is a key component in this process of maintaining a good soil structure.

HUMANE AND RESPONSIBLE TREATMENT OF LIVESTOCK

Livestock are an integral part of most organic systems, and care of livestock is extremely important. Animals are kept extensively rather than in factory farm units, are fed healthy organic food and are allowed to live as natural and fulfilling lives as can be made compatible with the farming system. More details about keeping animals are given in a separate section on pages 80–82.

AN EXTENSIVE MIXED FARMING SYSTEM

There are a very few producers who manage to run specialised organic systems, for example growing tomatoes under glass or running a sheep farm. Indeed, the basis of organic farming is that it should be both extensive and mixed. This is in direct opposition to the mainstream trend since the Second World War, which has been towards specialisation and intensification. Single-crop intensive farms look good on paper, but end up with many problems in practice; as we have already seen, this can include widespread soil erosion and an increasing reliance on agrochemicals.

The fact that the European Community has now introduced an extensification programme for farms shows how far the thinking of conventional farming policymakers has moved against the intensive system. Organic farming is reflecting the spirit of the 21st century.

CHARTER FOR ORGANIC AGRICULTURE

These, then, are the essential building blocks of the organic system, but they are by no means the full story. Organic farmers see themselves as an integral part of the green movement (and, in some ways, its precursor). This means that organic farming has to take account of many other environmental and social issues, such as energy use, transport, employment, nature conservation, access and landscape.

A few years ago, the Soil Association joined with other organic organisations in producing a Charter for Organic Agriculture that laid out the wider issues that organic farming attempts to include. The text of the Charter is given in full below.

> The current crisis of overproduction is a threat, not just to the European Community but to the stability of British agriculture, both now and in the future. The livelihood, and indeed survival, of British farmers, and through them of the whole fabric of agriculture and rural society, is now seriously threatened.
>
> Unless there is a series of fundamental reforms, the crisis will only get worse. We therefore call upon all who are involved in determining the future of agriculture, food quality and the environment to support the principles of this Charter.
>
> The Charter urges people to pledge to:
> 1. Ensure that all production and the management of farm resources are in harmony, rather than in conflict, with the natural system.
> 2. Use and develop technology appropriate to an understanding of biological systems.
> 3. Rely primarily on renewable energy and rotations to achieve and maintain soil fertility for optimum production.
> 4. Aim for optimum nutritional value of all staple foods.
> 5. Encourage decentralised systems for processing, distribution and marketing of farm products.

6. Strive for an equitable relationship between those
    who work and live on the land and, by maintaining
    wildlife and its habitats, create a countryside which
    is aesthetically pleasing for all.

7
WHAT FOODS ARE GROWN ORGANICALLY?

At the moment, the commonest organic foods are fruit, vegetables and grain products such as bread and biscuits. However, there is also a rapidly growing demand for organic meat, and organic drinks such as wine and beer. Some of these are looked at in more detail in the sections below.

Any food can be grown organically, although there may be greater constraints on where and when particular crops can be raised successfully. At the moment the main plant crops are market garden vegetables, grains and some fruits. Organic holdings in Britain tend to be either run wholly as market gardens or as farms; in the latter case produce includes meat, dairy produce, and field vegetables such as peas and various types of grain, although some farms also incorporate a garden and covered greenhouses.

Some of the most popular organic foods are salad vegetables, root vegetables and grain. The existence of pesticide residues on wholegrain bread has meant that there is a rapidly increasing market in fully organic brown bread. There are also a number of organic herb growers in Britain, producing herbs for both culinary and medicinal purposes.

It is part of the principles of organic food production that it should be consumed with as little processing as possible. None the less, there are some acceptable processed foods that are increasingly becoming available as organic produce: bread, biscuits, a range of pastas and other products made with flour; cheeses, yoghurts and other dairy produce; breakfast cereals; and spreads.

Most organic farmers also include livestock on their farms (the issue of organic food and vegetarianism is discussed in more detail on page 100). This results in the production of dairy produce and meat, both of which are discussed below. More recently there has been an increase in interest in two specific types of produce that don't fall quite so neatly into the system described above; these are organic cotton and organic wine, both of which are examined at the end of the chapter.

ORGANIC MEAT

Having stressed that organic doesn't just mean stepping back in time, this is precisely what it does mean in some ways with regard to meat production. Organic producers have deliberately turned their backs on some of the worst excesses of intensive meat production; instead they use the best aspects of traditional methods to produce meat, with an emphasis on good taste and good treatment of animals. At the same time, the animals have access to modern medicines and other humane innovations that can improve the quality of their lives.

Organic meat comes from animals that are reared in traditional ways, with an emphasis on maintaining high standards of welfare. This means providing adequate living space and bedding, with access to open pasture. Mothers are allowed to rear their offspring for longer than in many conventional systems, thus being able to express their natural behavioural instincts. Transport of animals, when it occurs at all, is managed carefully to avoid stress. Any mutilation, such as the debeaking of chickens, is banned.

Growth promoters have never been allowed for organic livestock. Although these are currently banned for all farmers in Europe, this may change under new trade laws, whereupon the stand taken by organic farmers will become important again. There are also strict controls over the use of veterinary medicines; rather than reaching for powerful drugs to compensate for unhealthy animals created by poor living conditions, the emphasis in organic production is placed on avoiding stress and keeping animals naturally healthy. This is achieved through good food, plenty of space and fresh air, and adequate shelter. This in itself cuts out the need for many of the medicines routinely added to food in intensive units. People who have converted to organic methods generally find their animals are healthier and less susceptible to disease, especially if they were previously farmed under an intensive system.

On the relatively rare occasions when illness does occur, or a particular disease threatens an organic farm, conventional medication is allowed, but when this does happen an extended period for detoxification must pass before the animal regains its organic status under the Soil Association symbol. These 'withdrawal periods' are up to seven times as long as the statutory minimum listed by the drug companies. When treatment is a legal requirement, as in dipping sheep for fly strike, only the least toxic pesticides are permitted.

In addition, organic farmers are encouraged, but not obliged, to try treatment methods not involving the use of powerful drugs, ideally in cooperation with a sympathetic vet. For example, many organic farmers use homoeopathic remedies, and there are a growing number of veterinary surgeons who are willing or eager to use these wherever possible. The emphasis is on what is good for the animal rather than any doctrinaire approach, and there are strict obligations that a sick or suffering animal is treated promptly and adequately.

The other major difference between organic and conventional livestock is that animals reared under an organic system must, as far as possible, be fed on organic food. Much of the time they are out to pasture, of course, and this must itself be managed as part of an approved organic system. During periods when the animals need extra food, most of this must come from an organic system, although, because of the problems in getting hold of supplies, a certain amount of some conventionally produced foods is permitted. But animal protein, including meat and bonemeal, feather-meal, manure, etc., and also solvent-extracted feeds, are all banned under an organic system. Furthermore, all food must be adequately labelled to ensure that the farmer knows precisely what is being fed to the animals. Usually, at least 70–90 per cent of the animals' food must be fully organic.

An increasing number of animal welfare groups are supporting the Soil Association's organic standards for meat production. The Farm and Food Society, for example, has a place on the committee setting livestock standards. At the moment, customer surveys suggest that few people buy organic food because of the high animal welfare standards and the Soil Association has been increasing its publicity about this aspect of the symbol scheme.

ORGANIC WINE AND OTHER ALCOHOL

The production of organic wine differs from other areas of organic farming because it is impossible to grow grape vines on a regular rotation. This means that grape production cannot be as fully organic as most producers would like. On the other hand, the reduction in some of the additives used in conventional wine has an immediate effect on the experience of many wine drinkers, in that it reduces the chance of getting a hangover, so that even people who are not interested in organic food for any other reason are seeking out organic wine.

In an organic vine system, soil fertility is maintained by managed use of manures and composts. Most pesticides are banned, but limited use of Bordeaux mixture (copper sulphate) and sulphur dioxide is allowed to prevent growth of mould. Sulphur dioxide is also allowed during the process of vinification (wine making) to stop the wine turning to vinegar, but organic standards only allow, at most, a quarter of the legal maximum of sulphur dioxide used in conventional wine making.

These changes have two immediate effects. Vines grown under the intensive system are increasingly sprayed with pesticides, and some people experience an allergic reaction, this being especially common in bronchial and asthmatic sufferers. With organic wines this problem doesn't arise. Furthermore, the low levels of sulphur dioxide used in organic wine reduce the probability and/or severity of a hangover.

Many organic wines are favoured by vegetarians and vegans because in most cases animal products are not used in the process of fining (i.e. removing all the detritus such as yeast cells, grape particles, etc.). However you should check with the importer or manufacturer, because a few organic wines do use animal products such as isinglass (sturgeon's airbladders), dried ox-blood powder or the white of eggs. Most organic wine importers show which of their wines contain animal products.

There are also a few organic beers, made from organically grown hops and brewed without chemical additives (many beers such as stouts are artificially dyed, for example). These still have a small share of the market, although they are starting to be sold at specialist outlets in Britain. There are also a range of organic ciders and many fully organic soft drinks.

ORGANIC COTTON

Chemical agriculture doesn't just affect the food we eat. At the moment, cotton is one of the most intensively farmed products on earth. Some estimates suggest that up to a quarter of all pesticides used today are sprayed on cotton. This has two effects; it causes an enormous amount of environmental damage, and it means that some residues end up in cotton clothes. There is a belief, although admittedly one that hasn't been tested very vigorously as yet, that sensitive people now suffer allergies as a result of wearing cloth containing high pesticide residue levels.

There is a small, but growing, market in organic cotton,

although supplies are still strictly limited. However there
are now plans for a massive increase in organic cotton, and
several designers and clothes manufacturers in Britain
have expressed interest.

OTHER ORGANIC PRODUCTS

Indeed, there is a growing interest in organic methods
throughout the third world, which means an increasing
supply of organic produce. You can now buy Tanzanian
organic tea, Mexican organic coffee, Zambian organic
honey (produced so far from industry that it can be
guaranteed truly organic), Pakistani organic rice, and so
on. The Soil Association is involved in all these
developments, through its foreign verification scheme
(described on page 119) and through its active membership
of the International Federation of Organic Agriculture
Movements, which seeks to help farmers anywhere in the
world change over to organic production.

8
IS ORGANIC FARMING GOOD FOR THE ENVIRONMENT?

When Lady Eve Balfour and her colleagues first talked about establishing the Soil Association in the 1940s, they saw two principal advantages to organic agriculture – better food and a more sustainable farming system. The Soil Association has always been convinced that an organic farming system had great environmental beliefs. Research carried out during the 1980s gave substantial scientific credence to these gut feelings, and the environmentally friendlier nature of organic agriculture is now generally acknowledged.

Note, 'environmentally friendlier' rather than 'environmentally friendly'. No modern farming system can be described as wholly environmentally friendly, because it involves stressing and stretching the natural system to produce large amounts of food for human beings. Farming inevitably disturbs wildlife and natural systems during production. Any cultivation results in greater risks of soil erosion, some leaching of materials away from the field, and destruction of natural plants and animals. Any livestock farming involves confining animals to some extent and, in most cases, eventually killing them. Keeping cows in milk and chickens laying eggs is an inherently unnatural process. While organic farming reduces the environmental impacts very considerably, it can never eliminate all effects and all risks.

CUTTING OUT PESTICIDES

First, of course, organic methods cut out all but a tiny number of pesticides. As we've already seen in the discussions about spray drift and wildlife (see pages 45–47, 52) this removes an enormous threat to wild plants and animals. Research in Denmark and a preliminary study in the UK by the British Trust for Ornithology show that both the number and the variety of wild birds increases on an organic farm, as compared to a chemical farm.

The study by the Game Conservancy on survival of grey partridge chicks, quoted earlier, also found that numbers of butterflies and other insects, and of smaller birds, quickly built up when pesticide spray drift was eliminated. This study didn't take place on an organic system, but on farms where spraying was simply reduced a little bit. It is to be expected that overall effects would be even greater on an organic farm.

The Game Conservancy work is important because it shows that pesticides have wider effects than simply on the plants and animals they kill. These indirect, or secondary, effects can be extremely important; for example, even if a farmer uses a pesticide that is specific to only one particular pest, this will have knock-on effects on predators of that pest (which suddenly won't have anything to eat), on their predators, on the plants they help to pollinate, on their parasites, and so on. An increasing number of organic farmers are trying to eliminate all pesticides from their systems, including the new relatively non-toxic pesticides passed by the Soil Association standards, because of the longer term damage their use has on the preventative methods of pest control.

Use of organic methods also means that there is no leaching of pesticides into ditches, rivers or streams. In the case of sheep dipping, which is required by law, organic farmers are obliged to use the safest possible pesticides available, thus minimising the risks to fish and otters, both of which have suffered badly from poisoning over the last few decades.

THE NITRATE CONNECTION

Another advantage that became increasingly relevant during the 1980s is that there is increasingly strong evidence that organic methods, if practised correctly, will substantially cut down nitrate leaching from farmland.

The precise mechanics of nitrate leaching are still not fully understood. The fertiliser manufacturers insist that the nitrate lost from farmland comes as a result of ploughing rather than application of soluble nitrate fertiliser. Other people think that the fertilisers themselves add to the problem; this is tacitly admitted by the government and the officials at the Ministry of Agriculture, who advise farmers to cut out the autumn dressing of fertiliser to reduce nitrate losses. Whatever the pathway followed by the nitrate, everyone agrees that intensive farming systems have increased the amount of nitrate leaching into freshwater.

During the second half of the 1980s a lot of research was carried out into the potential for reducing nitrate leaching through the use of organic systems. The pressure for change came from the European Community, which has imposed maximum levels for nitrate in drinking water. These levels are frequently being broken in Britain, and when the government finally faced up to its legal responsibilities and started taking nitrate pollution seriously, organic farming was one of the options considered. At first sight, organic farming should be much less likely to cause nitrate leaching because it cuts out all soluble nitrate fertilisers, although there are a number of other factors to be taken into account.

Work carried out at Elm Farm Research Centre, and elsewhere, found that on average nitrate leaching could be reduced by about three-quarters on a well managed organic farm; this is an average because, when the legume crop is ploughed in or the pasture ploughed, there is always a 'pulse' of nitrate released, which may well end up in freshwater. However, the rotation means that only a fairly small proportion of the farmland will be ploughed up at any one time. Because nitrate leaching is considerably reduced for the rest of the rotation, overall leaching rates fall substantially.

The Soil Association has been involved in lobbying for organic methods to be included amongst the preferred options for management in nitrate sensitive areas, the land areas in Britain identified as needing crisis management to reduce nitrate pollution. This still hasn't been agreed by the government, despite the Elm Farm research being sponsored by the Department of the Environment, although there is a good chance that the organic option will soon be included in NSA regulations.

KEEPING THE SOIL

Organic farming is also proving to be a better custodian of the soil than intensive chemical methods. As the global issue of soil erosion becomes politically important again, this aspect is gaining an increasing amount of attention, especially in the Third World.

Organic farming offers a number of clear advantages to soil health, including:

- Use of farming methods that build up the amount of humus in the soil, through green manuring, composts and rotations.
- Not using agrochemicals that are likely to destroy soil life, and thus reduce the health of the soil itself.
- Keeping or recreating small fields, with hedges and other solid boundaries that reduce the amount of wind erosion.
- Maintaining plant cover on the soil for as much of the year as possible, which again helps stop erosion by wind and rain.
- Including pasture in many rotations, thus allowing the soil a period with minimal losses, in which it has time to build up again.
- Using generally smaller machinery, which compacts the earth less, and reducing the number of times that the tractor passes over a field.

A study in the United States compared soil on an established organic farm with that on an adjoining chemical farm, both with the same basic soil history and profile. The soil on the organic farm was found to have a humus layer 16 times the depth of that from the chemical neighbour, and to suffer considerably less soil erosion as a result. In another experiment, comparing adjacent organic and conventional farms, which was carried out over 37 years, the conventionally-managed field lost more than four times as much topsoil. Similar studies have not been undertaken in Britain, but there is no reason to suppose that the results would be much different.

As long ago as 1980 the United States Department of Agriculture (USDA) was noting that many management practices followed by organic farmers are those highly recommended by the USDA itself for improving the productivity and tilth of the soil. Of course, many 'conventional' farmers also practise some of the techniques used by their organic counterparts, and can reduce their soil erosion as a result, but the primary emphasis put on soil health by organic farmers is likely to minimise erosion risks.

WILDLIFE

Wildlife is not a luxury for the organic farmer, but an essential part of the farming system. Organic farming encourages wildlife both because it eliminates almost all the chemicals that harm wild plants and animals, and because it encourages a production system that includes hedgerows, wild areas, mixed pasture and clean rivers and streams. Several studies have shown that there is increased wildlife on organic farms when compared with conventional farms, and we've summarised some of these earlier in the book.

However, until recently there has been no specific guarantee that organic farmers would look after natural areas on their farms any more sensitively than conventional farmers. Most do, because care of the environment is one of the reasons that they become organic farmers in the first place. But with more farmers converting, and with growing interest in conservation issues in Britain, the Soil Association has now incorporated a special environment and conservation standard into the rules and guidelines followed by all Soil Association symbol-holders. These were worked out by the Soil Association in cooperation with over 20 other organic and nature conservation organisations, including the government's Nature Conservancy Council and the Countryside Commission. (For a more complete explanation of the standards and the symbol, see chapter 11.) The conservation standards are likely to be of interest to the non-technical reader and are reproduced in full.

The way the standards work is explained in more detail later. But what is important here is that, for the first time, we have a specific code for maximising the wildlife potential and protecting heritage, designed by farmers and conservationists working together, which is binding on the farmers holding the Soil Association symbol. The standards, and the accompanying *Guidelines for Conservation* which explain them in more detail, will continue to be developed in the coming years. They provide a model for similar work which could be carried out with other types of farmers in the future.

However, the Guidelines for Conservation are only part of the story. Since the Second World War, conservation organisations have been forced to retrench to the margins of agricultural land – to the hedges, copses and the few areas of unimproved land. The mass of agricultural land has been regarded as a sterile desert for wildlife, on to which plants and animals stray at their peril. But organic farmers and growers are now showing that it doesn't have to be like this.

Most farmers, conventional and organic, do care about the countryside. Farming methods are now being developed that mean that, as far as possible, the whole farm becomes a reservoir for wildlife. The advantages of this are obvious and enormous. There is a growing acknowledgment amongst conservation organisations that organic farming offers a real possibility of breaking the cycle of environmental destruction that has plagued the British agricultural countryside for so long.

THE SOIL ASSOCIATION CONSERVATION STANDARDS

In addition to the specific recommendations in the general production standards, symbol-holders are required to abide by legal and statutory requirements in respect to any aspect of the wider environment at all times.

Traditional field boundaries and hedge management

Recommended	Styles of hedges and stone walling in keeping with local traditions. Hedge laying. Hedge trimming once every three years. Ditch clearance in phased operations, maintaining a portion of ditches uncleared every year. Clearing opposite sides of ditches in successive years. Hedge trimming, ditch and dyke clearance between January and March.
Restricted	Removal of hedgerows and banks. Annual trimming of all hedges.
Prohibited	Hedge trimming, ditch and dyke clearance between the end of March and the beginning of September.

Pasture management

Old unimproved (species rich) meadows are an important habitat for many plants and insects. They are generally defined as having more than 40 per cent cover of broad-leaved herbs (excluding clover) and are usually over 10 years old.

These pastures make a useful contribution to organic livestock nutrition due to the diversity of plant species and high mineral and trace element content.

Recommended   Maintenance of established patterns of cropping.
Cutting of species-rich meadows in keeping with species requirements.

Restricted   Manure application on unimproved meadows should be no more than an average of 75 kg nitrogen/hectare/year or equivalent (for example approximately 25 tonnes of farmyard manure/hectare/year).

Prohibited   Ploughing of unimproved pastures agreed to be of conservation interest.

Moorland

Moorland, heathland and other areas of semi-natural vegetation such as scrub are so reduced in extent nationally as to have become of direct conservation interest and approval must be sought before they are in any way 'improved'.

Drainage

Prohibited   Drainage of wetland of significant conservation value.

Tree and woodland management

Trees and woodland play an important role in maintaining the ecological balance of organic farms. They provide habitat for wildlife including pest predators. Mature trees and woodland may also have an amenity and recreational value. Individual trees and ancient woodland play a vital part in preserving landscape and species diversity. Management of existing woodland should take into account these factors. New planting must be in keeping with existing landscape features and habitats. Monocropping with single-species stands should be avoided.

New planting should not take place on semi-natural or other good wildlife habitat, or other sites of particular ecological and archaeological interest.

Recommended   Replanting programmes integrated with existing woodlands and trees, and using indigenous and local shrubs and trees.
Natural regeneration.
Coppicing, and other traditional woodland management practices.
Fencing of woodland against stock.

Restricted   Clear felling of woodland.
Felling of mature specimen trees that are not diseased or endangering safety.

Buildings and archaeological sites
Farm buildings should be preserved in their original
state if at all possible.

The siting and construction of new farm buildings
should be done sensitively, taking account of their
environmental and aesthetic impact. Existing old
buildings should be maintained wherever possible in
their original form. In considering their conversion or
demolition it is recommended that advice from the
Society for the Protection of Ancient Buildings is
sought.

Recommended   Preservation of farm buildings in
          their original state.
          Use of local materials.
          The provision of roosts and nest
          sites for bats and barn owls in
          new buildings and conversions.

Prohibited   Levelling of ridge and furrow fields
          and cultivation of sites of ancient
          monuments, archaeological sites
          and earthworks.

9
IS ORGANIC FOOD BETTER FOR OUR HEALTH?

In 1939 the Committee Representing the Medical Practitioners of Cheshire drew up a joint statement about diet and health, which they called the *Medical Testament*. Despite the apparent obscurity of the source, this document is still important today, because it encapsulated much of the thinking of the radical nutritionists of the first half of the century, notably Sir Albert Howard and Robert McCarrison. It was quoted in total in the first chapter of Lady Eve Balfour's *The Living Soil*, the book which provided the impetus for creating the Soil Association. A key section of their testament states:

> There is some principle or quality in [traditional, healthy] diets which is absent from, or deficient in, the food of our people today ... the food is, for the most part, *fresh from its source, little altered by preparation and complete*; and that, in the case of those based on agriculture, the natural cycle:
>
> Animal and vegetable waste $\Bigg\}$ → Soil → Plant → Animal → Man
>
> is complete. No chemical or substitution stage intervenes. Sir Albert Howard ... has shown that the ancient Chinese method of returning to the soil, after treatment, the whole of the animal and vegetable refuse which is produced in the activities of the community

results in the health and productivity of crops and of the animals and men who feed thereon.

In other words, the doctors were saying that organically produced food (which is what they were describing, although they didn't use the name) was intrinsically better for health than food produced by chemical means. This view was shared by Lady Eve Balfour throughout her life, and is shared by many people who buy organic food today. But is there any evidence to back up this belief? Below, we look at some of the issues concerning organic food and health.

ACCIDENTAL CONTAMINATION OF FOOD

The first reason why many people buy organic food is that they are concerned about what they may inadvertently be buying with their conventional food, as a result of accidental contamination. This includes pesticide residues, higher than natural nitrate levels and, perhaps, residues from antibiotics and other drugs used on farm livestock.

Although this is the most obvious potential health benefit of organic food, unless you are one of those who believes that all residues are harmless, the truth is slightly more complicated. Organic produce should certainly be lower in accidental contaminants than conventional food, but there can be no guarantee that it will be completely free of unwanted chemical residues, as we have seen earlier (page 14). The Soil Association has always been careful to avoid using catch-phrases such as 'pesticide-free food' because, in the industrial world, it is impossible to ensure that anything is entirely uncontaminated. Organic food can be hit by pesticide spray drift, or contaminated by being stored next to conventional food, or from persistent pesticide residues which remain in the soil. If food is grown out of season, under glass, some crops are likely to build up high nitrate levels, whether or not they are organic (although it seems that those produced with artificial fertilisers are likely to have slightly higher nitrate levels).

This means that, for people worried about agrochemicals, organic food is a much better bet than conventional produce, but not entirely free of risk.

DELIBERATE ADULTERATION

We are on slightly firmer ground when we look at the risks from deliberate adulteration, including the use of additives, the over-processing of food, irradiation, the use of genetically manipulated organisms such as BST, and other problems which we summarised in Chapter 2. There is no serious doubt at all that diet is a major cause of ill health, and food additives, over-refined food, high saturated fat diets, high sugar diets, high salt diets are all blamed, with increasing authority, for a range of ailments including heart disease and cancer.

Any diet based on organic food addresses most of these problems. There will be minimal use of additives in any organic product. The Soil Association Standards are quite clear: Prohibited: All synthetic preservatives, colourants, sweeteners, flavour enhancers, emulsifiers and other synthetic additives. Organic food will thus never be irradiated; nor contain BST and other hormone substitutes; nor growth promoting hormones; nor excessive sugar, salt or other natural additives that can have ill effects on health if taken in excess.

There are some less obvious benefits to an organic diet as well. As explained earlier (page 38), meat from animals raised in an extensive system, fed largely on natural foods, will contain a lower proportion of saturated fats than meat raised under factory farming conditions.

FOOD AS IT SHOULD BE

It is, of course, quite possible to buy fresh unprocessed food from chemical farms. But, despite the advertisers' images of grocery stores and fruit stands, we are buying less and less fresh food, and more and more processed food, fast food, pre-packaged meals, sugar-drenched tinned foods, dried foods and, of course, chocolate and sweets.

Although some processed organic food does exist, this is in a minority. As the authors of the *Medical Treatment* wrote over 50 years ago, organic food should be 'fresh from its source, little altered by preparation and complete.' Matching theory to practice is difficult here, especially when organic foods are imported from abroad, but the philosophy underlining this remains, and most organic food is processed as little as possible or, in the case of foods such as bread and biscuits made from organic flour, processed without many of the extra additives that you get with most conventionally produced white or brown loaves.

BUT IS ALL PROCESSING BAD?

Most of the above would be seen as good commonsense by today's doctors and health specialists. The lessons of the last few decades of poor diet have been well learned, if not necessarily acted upon, and the need for good quantities of fresh raw uncontaminated food to maintain good health is now almost universally supported. But, with the exception of pesticide residues (which are still a contentious issue according to the agribusiness industry), couldn't we get just the same effect from a well-chosen conventional diet? Here, the proponents of organic food go one stage further, and say that we can't; in other words that organic food has positive health-giving properties, derived from the way in which it is produced, which are inevitably absent from conventionally produced foods.

The real milk issue

The debate about wholefood came to a head in the 1980s over an issue which involved both conventional and organic farmers – the attempts by successive British governments to ban the sale of unpasteurised green-top milk.

Pasteurisation, which is a heat treatment, was introduced to protect against tuberculosis and other bacterial infections, including salmonella. All well

---

and good. But there have always been a substantial section of the population who preferred to drink unpasteurised milk, from tuberculin tested herds, because they believed it tasted better and/or it was better for health. Raw milk was sold in special green-top milk bottles. The Queen drinks raw milk whenever possible.

Since the mid-1980s the government tried to limit the sale of raw milk altogether, first by banning anything except sales by direct delivery, and then proposing to ban it altogether. A campaign by the Association of Unpasteurised Milk Producers and Consumers, started and run by Soil Association Council member Sir Julian Rose, gathered enough momentum to stop the complete ban in 1989.

They won on the issue of freedom of choice, but there is also some evidence that raw milk has substantial nutritional advantages over pasteurised milk.

- Heat treatment destroys some of the nutritional value, with a 10 per cent loss of vitamins B6, B12 and folate, and a 25 per cent loss of vitamin C.
- It also causes the inactivation of some protein carriers, which are important for the uptake of zinc, vitamin B12 and folate, amongst other substances.
- The whey proteins themselves are destroyed.
- So are all the bacteria, and many of the bacteria in milk are good rather than bad. This also means that any reinfection by harmful bacteria after pasteurisation allows contamination to spread more rapidly than in raw milk.

All of these issues are open to debate with regard to their importance in the overall diet. However, the point should not be lost: many people choose raw milk because it is raw and as unprocessed as possible, and there is a body of evidence to suggest that raw milk is better for health than pasteurised milk.

THE POSITIVE HEALTH BENEFITS OF ORGANIC FOOD

This brings us to the last, much more controversial, point about organic food; that there is a small, but significant, body of evidence that suggests that it has positive health benefits as compared to non-organic food. There is undoubtedly still much work to be done in this area, and the Soil Association is initiating a major study on the links between organic food and health to run during the 1990s. It is very difficult to make firm judgements one way or the other until this work has been completed.

None the less, there are already a growing number of health specialists who are recommending organic food as part of a diet to counter allergies and particular health problems, and as part of a general therapy to tackle more serious diseases, including cancer. It would be irresponsible to say that a change in diet could cure all such life-threatening diseases. However, almost all doctors would agree that a general level of health is an essential part of combating any illness, and that a good diet is a vital part of maintaining or regaining health. The research carried out to date suggests that the role of organic food in this process can be important. The Soil Association's current project will continue to look carefully at Lady Eve Balfour's second belief – that organic food is good for the environment and good for human health.

ORGANIC FARMING AND VEGETARIANS

Many vegetarians support organic farming, both because of its environmental benefits and because conventional farming results in the deaths of large numbers of animals through pesticide poisoning, nitrate leaching and other forms of pollution. However, at the moment almost all organic farms include livestock and it is difficult to see, on a farm scale, how the whole cycle could work quickly and efficiently enough without having animals.

Because of the interest amongst vegetarians and vegans,

there is now some work on stockless organic farms, using green manuring systems and composts, both in Germany and at Elm Farm Research Centre in Berkshire. But it will be quite a few years before we know whether such systems are viable in the long term. In the meantime, the organic movement's advice to any non-meat eaters, wondering about whether they should buy organic produce or not, is summed up in this extract from a paper prepared for the Vegan Society in 1987:

> The relationship between crop growing (ie. *plant* food production) and the destruction of wildlife is a crucial one for anybody concerned with the ethics of our treatment of animals. It is not generally realised that growing cereals and vegetables probably causes more animal deaths in Britain than any other single-factor ... Countless millions of invertebrates are killed every year of course, the vast majority having no damaging effects on plants at all. But the slaughter doesn't end there. Small mammals and birds are killed when they eat poisoned insects, or run through a freshly sprayed field, or when their food plants disappear ... Seen against this background of constant destruction, the animals deliberately slaughtered for meat are like a handful of sand compared to a whole beach.

Of course, there are many things that vegetarians and vegans will continue to find unpalatable about organic farming, including the keeping and slaughtering of animals, and the use of blood and bonemeal for fertiliser. Research may throw up options for totally animal-free farms in the future. But, on balance, there is a clear argument for all non-meat eaters to be eating organic food at the moment.

10
CAN ORGANIC FARMING FEED THE WORLD?

This is all very well. Organic farming might be better for wildlife and the countryside; it might give us slightly cleaner food; and it might salve our consciences a little about the conditions of farm animals when we tuck into an organic sausage. But surely this is all just middle-class western self-indulgence, isn't it? Most people in the world would be glad of the opportunity of eating sufficient quantities of nutritious food, even if it meant eating a tiny amount of pesticide at the same time. Won't organic farming, with its massively lower yields, simply mean that poor people get even less to eat?

As organic farming gains in popularity, we hear more and more arguments like this. The attacks on organic agriculture from the agrochemical industry, and others interested in maintaining the status quo of intensive agriculture, become progressively tougher. A common figure once quoted by the chemical industry is that if we stopped using pesticides tomorrow productivity would drop by 65 per cent in the first year, and continue to fall even further thereafter. Now it has become obvious that organic farms don't get overrun by pests, the argument has shifted to claim that organic farms are protected by the pesticides sprayed by their chemical neighbours. The general impression given is that we would all starve within months if we turned Britain, or anywhere else, over to more than a small proportion of organic farms.

This attitude becomes even more hardened when the agriculture of the third world is considered. The existing

problems of hunger and malnutrition can only be
conquered, say the chemical farming proponents, by a
massive intensification of agriculture. But is this really
true? Is organic farming really destined to be confined to a
few cranky part-time farmers in rich countries, supplying
a minority of neurotic or gullible middle-class customers.

HOW MUCH?

Over the last few years, a number of official and
independent research establishments have turned their
attention towards organic farming, and compared
productivity on organic and chemical farms in similar
areas, with similar soils and climates, and growing broadly
the same range of crops. The results surprised many
doubters. Let's consider a few examples.

In the United States the highly respected National
Academy of Sciences, based in Washington, DC, looked at
a whole range of organic and other less intensive farming
systems. They compared a number of farms, and found
that production levels were broadly similar when
conventional and organic farms are assessed. Their report,
Alternative Agriculture, was blunt:

> Well managed alternative farms use less synthetic
> chemical fertilisers, pesticides and antibiotics without
> necessarily decreasing – and in some cases increasing –
> per acre crop yields and the productivity of livestock
> systems ...
>
> Wide adoption of proven alternative systems would
> result in even greater economic benefits to farmers and
> environmental gains to the nation.

The report, which runs to many hundred pages, is a
comprehensive and damning refutation of the intensive
farming philosophy. However, it does not just concentrate
on organic farming, but looks at a range of low-input and
less intensive methods.

More recently the University of Kassel, in Germany,
has looked at the productivity of a range of organic and

conventional farms. They found a decrease in productivity of around 15 per cent on organic as compared to conventional farms. On the other hand, research shows that organic farms use less energy and resources, and create less pollution, so the actual value of the food is greater if the hidden costs are brought into the calculation. Their results fall broadly into line with those from other studies in Europe and the United States. Some studies even show organic and conventional production methods level-pegging in terms of productivity.

There have, to date, been no such comprehensive surveys carried out in Britain. We could be pessimistic, and say that productivity would fall slightly more here on average, because the intensification process has gone further in Britain than in most other European countries. But on the other hand, we are learning about organic methods all the time, and productivity is continuing to increase. The argument that we must have intensive chemical methods to feed the world simply doesn't hold water.

Some organic farmers now say that the conversion process is only complete when the productivity is the same as it was before they started. It will take some time, because it is only when the rest of the farm is in balance, when predators of pests have built up and the soil is in good shape, that the high yields return. The real conversion period to organic agriculture takes longer than the two years insisted on in organic standards.

THINGS ARE CHANGING ANYWAY

These arguments also have to be put into a political and environmental perspective. Current changes in farming are already helping reduce some of the most intensive practices. This trend will continue. The range of conservation regulations, including the new nitrate sensitive areas, environmentally sensitive areas, and regulations setting maximum levels for pesticide residues in water, have already been mentioned. They are already changing farming practice dramatically in some places, and will continue to change it in the future.

Just as important, at least in the short term, is the fact that we actually produce too much food in Europe, due to the crazy way in which the EC Common Agricultural Policy sets its grants. Everyone has heard about the butter mountains and the wine lakes. The CAP policy of promising to pay fixed prices for commodities has meant that farmers have been encouraged (and, because of other economic pressures, often effectively forced) to produce more and more food. Despite some efforts to counter this, the surpluses remain at the start of the 1990s. In 1989 everyone in Britain paid an average of £139 to get rid of unwanted food, and that doesn't even include the costs of subsidising growing it in the first place, or the environmental costs.

To counter these problems, the European Commission has introduced a system of extensification, to pay farmers to reduce productivity on land. Individual countries are left with the task of implementing this, and the actual steps proposed to date have remained weak in most cases. In Britain, for example, farmers and landowners are being paid to 'set aside' land, i.e. to leave it, doing nothing to it, for a few years. But this solves nothing, and may actually encourage farmers to intensify on other areas to get the same productivity as before, plus the set-aside payments. It is also politically embarrassing; having paid farmers to produce too much for years, we are now paying a few of them to produce less (and the rest to continue to produce more). The situation is not as simple as this, but this is the general public perception.

This will change, will have to change. The extensification programme may be weak at the moment, but there is a gradual, and painful, realisation that the party is over for the kind of intensive agriculture that has been practised in a continually accelerating manner, since the Second World War. The very word extensification is important in a symbolic way; it is the direct opposite of the intensification that we have lived with for so long, and is a tacit admission that the intensive road is not working properly.

Future schemes are being discussed, involving the whole farm and which promote a less intensive form of agriculture – virtually organic agriculture in fact. These schemes will not be introduced tomorrow, and will certainly not be introduced without a fight. But the changes have started, and are being acknowledged by the farming establishment.

SO, HOW MUCH?

So, once again, how much could we produce by organic methods in Britain? As stated before, we still can't say for sure. Methods are improving all the time; we will learn as we go along. No one is suggesting converting all land immediately, so there remains the possibility of proper research and development.

Nic Lampkin, of Aberystwyth University, has calculated the likely changes to agricultural productivity in Britain if we converted a fifth of Britain's farmland to organic agricultural methods, given what we now know about productivity. These are preliminary results, but show a theoretical snapshot of what we could do right now if we could carry out such a magical conversion. They are summarised in the accompanying table, and show that, in real terms, there would be very few significant changes in output. Certainly, given the amount of food we waste in unnecessary processing, bad transportation systems and poor marketing, these fade into insignificance. This is also true when such changes are compared with the over-production in Europe as a whole. These figures will be disputed by the agrochemical industry and others with a vested interest in maintaining the high input route to agriculture. None the less, they are being increasingly backed up by solid research, undertaken by independent research establishments, which suggest that organic farming really can come up with the bacon (and the grain, the milk, the vegetables, etc.).

Changes in output with 20 per cent conversion to organic agriculture in the UK

Land use	Relative change (percentage)
Cereals	− 6.02
Potatoes	− 2.58
Sugar beet	−11.62
Legumes	+34.84
Oil-seed rape	−12.10
Milk	− 3.80
Beef	− 2.62
Sheep	− 3.70

20 PER CENT BY 2000

In 1989 the Soil Association launched a campaign for 20 per cent organic by the year 2000 – to convert a fifth of Britain's farmland to organic methods by the end of the century. Unrealistic? We don't think so. Twenty per cent is roughly the figure that analysts think may be the organic food share of the retail market by then; it might well be higher if the price dropped more. It is also the proportion of Britain's farmland that is inevitably going to face radical changes in land use because of the various environmental and social changes and regulations outlined above. In many cases, the choice on these areas may either be a switch to organic farming or taking the land out of agriculture altogether and converting it to housing, golf courses and the like. Farmers want change, or at least see it as inevitable. Many would like to be farming organically, but cannot see how they can afford to do so, especially during the conversion period when land is no longer farmed conventionally but does not yet have full organic status. Reaching such a target would require a colossal change in farming practice, but some colossal change looks increasingly inevitable.

Patrick Holden, director of British Organic Farmers,

introduced the 20 per cent by 2000 campaign in a special editorial in the Soil Association's journal *Living Earth*:

> For the Soil Association, 20 per cent by 2000 is far from a wild dream. It is an imperative if we are to reverse the ecological consequences of half a century of agricultural exploitation. The end may be clear, but the means are not yet agreed and will be the subject of intense debate. Let us hope that the great philosophy which led to the formation of the Soil Association in 1946 can help change the world for the better as we move into the last crucial decade of this century.

Twenty per cent is not an end in itself. The Soil Association believes that most farming will end up organic in the future, as the advantages become clearer. Twenty per cent is merely a marker for future change.

SO WHAT ARE THE BLOCKS TO ORGANIC FARMING?

The Soil Association has been receiving hundreds of serious enquiries from farmers interested in converting to organic methods every month. But although the area of land under organic methods doubled during 1990, this still represents only a tiny proportion of those farmers expressing interest. What is going wrong?

Unfortunately, there are still a number of serious blocks to people converting to organic farming. One of the biggest is the fear that the farmer will not be able to survive the conversion period, when productivity falls (and it may fall considerably in the first couple of years until the system stabilises) and there is no premium.

Conversion is certainly a problem. In addition, Soil Association farmers are also expected to carry many other hidden financial burdens, including the time spent to maintain wildlife on farms. At the moment, they also lose out on many of the price incentives that other farmers receive. Accordingly, the Soil Association, in line with an increasing number of other farming and conservation groups, is calling for a switch in farm support, from supporting fixed prices for produce to supporting farming systems. Support would only be paid if the farm satisfied other requirements as well, such as having conservation value, access for leisure activities such as walking, good environmental protection in terms of minimising pollution, and so on. This would not only help farmers to convert, but would also help maintain farms in the long term as more than mere food factories. This type of whole-farm support for systems, rather than produce, received support from the European Commission in December 1990, and looks set to become the new method of farm funding in the future.

Another problem is the high price that organic food costs in some shops, which is seen as a limiting factor to an expansion of organic production methods. This is certainly a problem in some areas, but it is not inherent. Food prices today bear very little resemblance to the real value of food, or to what the farmer gets at the farm gate. Increased costs for organic food are caused partly by the factors described above, partly by the fact that a lot of our organic food is imported (itself totally ungreen) and partly because of the economics of scale; it is very expensive to move the small units of organic food from individual farms around the country. With more organic farmers, improved marketing and a better distribution system, this will change. Several large retail stores are already committed to dropping substantially the price of organic food in the near future.

The third block on organic farming, and one that is a real problem for many farmers, is that it remains a very different philosophy of farming. Going organic takes time, commitment and a lot of re-learning of agricultural practice. The would-be organic farmer has recourse to a growing number of college courses, independent groups such as the Organic Advisory Service, and producer organisations, but there is still a dearth of cheap, accessible information, and nothing like the wealth of free or cheap advice that is available to the chemical farmer.

All these blocks can be overcome with time, money and a little bit of political willpower. It is to achieve these ends that the Soil Association's 20 per cent by 2000 campaign has been established.

BUT WHAT ABOUT THE THIRD WORLD?

As we argued in Chapter 5, the types of farming being promoted in the third world by western industrial interests are not necessarily going to solve any problems. Certainly an increasing number of farmers in Africa, Asia and Latin America want nothing to do with the agrochemicals that they can hardly afford, and which are destroying their health.

Many of these farmers are looking towards organic methods. An increasing number of governments in the third world are carrying out extensive research programmes, using the best of traditional agricultural methods, along with new techniques developed by organic farmers in the north and south. Interest is growing, as are the number of successful producers.

It would be grossly over-simplistic to say that, because organic methods work in the temperate north, they will automatically work just as well in the south. Conditions are harsher, environmental damage is in some cases already much more severe; we simply don't know what will be necessary in the future, and all options have to be looked at carefully. But organic agriculture should be one of those options. The north has spent the last few decades lecturing to the south about how it should improve its 'primitive' agriculture. But much of this advice has been powered by vested interests with things to sell and profits to make. We have made things worse by our attitudes to debt, by our financial relationships with the south and by our scandalous misuse of much aid money. There is not sufficient space here to discuss these issues in detail, but there is a clear need for a change of attitude towards agriculture in the third world. The organic option has to be one important new element in our thinking. And it is already being considered by many third world countries themselves.

The Soil Association is part of this process of change. Our education project, Organic Agriculture: The Development Option, concentrates on teaching aid agencies, development workers and others in the north about the potential of organic agriculture in the south. Much of this is pitched at a very simple level – how to make compost; simple pest control methods; the use of a rotation in tropical agriculture, and so on. This means that at least the teachers and consultants we send to the south are not promoting a wholly one-sided view of agricultural development. It includes details of successful organic projects in the third world, and shows what can be done without the use of expensive and hazardous imported agrochemicals.

But much more is needed: a diversion of a proportion of aid research funding to look specifically at the organic option in selected tropical and subtropical countries; non-chemical pest control methods suitable for use in particular habitats and climates, and against specific pests; expanding the range of crops grown so that we are not relying on less than a dozen key crops for the bulk of our food everywhere, and can thus never get the advantages of using species adapted to particular localities; simple tools such as hand-weeders or tillers to replace pesticides.

There are steps being taken in this direction but, with the exception of a few United Nations' funded projects, they are mainly being undertaken by individuals, lacking proper funding and equipment. The political aspects of control of agricultural research make it difficult to promote radical shifts in thinking. There is much work still to be done.

CONCLUSIONS

So, we don't yet know if organic farming is the answer everywhere. We know it can work in the north, and can supply sufficient food. We think that it can work in the south but, in the rush to intensify the agriculture of the third world, we have still hardly looked at the possibilities.

The agribusiness industry will continue to deny that there is any role for organic agriculture. As this book was entering its final stages, another agrochemical leaflet came out, saying 'Adopting organic farming across the board is simply a recipe for world hunger'. These industry voices are sounding increasingly desperate. The Soil Association hopes that, with growing public interest all over the world, and with more and more evidence that organic farming can and does work in real situations, it will start to get a fair hearing at last.

RESOURCES

This section gives information on organic food standards,
where to obtain organic food, and recommends
particularly useful books for further information. This is
followed by practical advice on how to grow organic food
for yourself.

For further reading and useful addresses, see page 150.

11
HOW TO IDENTIFY GOOD ORGANIC FOOD

Quite a lot of the people reading this book will already be buying some organic food. You'll almost certainly be paying extra for the privilege. But how do you know that it is really organic? The ways of guaranteeing genuine organic food have occupied the worldwide organic movement for some time and have, incidentally, given us a lot of experience that is being utilised by people wanting to devise 'environmentally friendlier' eco-labels for other produce.

Indeed, the Soil Association is now best known as the main organisation running an organic symbol in Britain. There are now (1991) well over 500 symbol-holder farmers and growers in Britain, and a growing foreign verification programme. The symbol is also awarded to certain certification schemes in other countries, if they meet the same standards as the Soil Association scheme. Interest is running very high at the moment, and several hundred farmers a month are applying for information about the symbol scheme. It is, therefore, central to the whole running of the Association.

WHY A CERTIFICATION SYSTEM?

As soon as the market for organic food started to expand, so did the risk of fraud. As long as people are prepared to pay extra for something labelled 'organic', then unfortunately there are going to be a few unscrupulous farmers and traders prepared to stick an organic label on something grown using all the pesticides under the sun. Unless this is controlled, organic food itself will become devalued, as has happened in the case of eggs, where it is estimated that over half the 'free range' eggs sold in Britain actually come from battery units.

In the 1970s organic farmers and growers in Britain (and in many other countries) began to realise that they needed to be able to guarantee that food sold as 'organic' really was produced by organic methods. The Soil Association became involved in this debate. At first, the answer seemed simple. An independent certification organisation should prepare a set of standards for organic farmers to produce by, should inspect the farms and should award a special quality label to those who measured up to expectations. (Older readers will be able to remember the cheerful little lion that used to appear on all genuine British-farmed eggs – a similar scheme.)

However, setting standards has proved a lot more difficult than anyone imagined. For one thing, no one had really tried to define, in detail, exactly what constituted 'organic farming'. The basic principles were fairly clear, but this still left a lot of very grey areas. Which pesticides should be allowed, if any? Was animal welfare included? Precisely which kinds of 'natural' fertilisers should be permitted? Inevitably, the result of such uncertainty meant that almost every country ended up with a slightly different definition of organic agriculture, and therefore different regulations for the growers. There were often, as in the case of Britain, competing definitions, and a number of standards operating in one country.

This is unsatisfactory. It confuses governments, farmers and consumers, and causes unnecessary rifts within what is already a small and underfunded group of individuals. Arguments in Britain over such things as the use of Chilean nitrate on organic systems gained the organic movement the reputation of division and in-fighting at just the time when it needed to pull together to promote organic agriculture to a wide, and still largely uninterested, agricultural community. It allowed those people sceptical of, or opposed to, organic farming to make out that the rifts were bigger than they really were in practice.

None the less, the debates about standards were crucial to the development of the science and practice of organic agriculture. For the first time ever, people were trying to define a method of food production systematically and completely. To make things even more difficult, the definition has been successively widened to embrace many other issues that concern people buying organic food, such as the way that animals are housed and treated, the way food is processed after it has been grown, the wider environmental effects of the farming practice, and so on. In the days before it was fashionable, the organic movement was carrying out an extensive environmental audit of the whole organisation of organic agriculture.

This process has not been time wasted. Farming in general is being forced to become less narrow in scope. Whilst successive governments since the Second World War have effectively told farmers to treat their land like a food factory, this attitude is at last changing, and changing fast, as we have seen. The existence of food surpluses, mounting environmental pollution and additional pressures on the land are forcing a massive turnaround in attitudes to farming.

SOIL ASSOCIATION STANDARDS AND THE SOIL ASSOCIATION SYMBOL

Over a period since about the mid-1970s, the Soil Association standards have gradually developed into a system that is widely respected by farmers, government and consumers.

The standards are set by a number of committees, made up of people from a range of organic organisations and including many professional farmers and growers. The standards themselves are laid out in a fairly weighty manual that gives rules and guidance notes covering a wide range of issues, including: what is and is not allowed in growing systems; the type of system that should be followed, and how and when; standards for livestock (including what they should be fed and detailed welfare rules); regulations governing processing and packaging; and so on. Separate standards are defined for particular products.

Different practices are categorised as one of the following – recommended, permitted, restricted and prohibited. The only one of these that requires further amplification is 'restricted', a category that usually refers to a practice which can be used sometimes, in an emergency, but only if an individual producer obtains special permission from the appropriate committee. This is a laborious, but vital, element in the standards; it means that the symbol doesn't become so idealistic that it is unworkable, while at the same time it stops the floodgates of relaxed standards and compromise. For example, an organic grower is allowed to use one of a small range of plant-based pesticides in an emergency; but if someone wants to apply pesticides every year, because of some particular recurrent problem, they have to put their case to the symbol committee, which is the final arbiter about whether this is allowable or not.

Once a farmer or market gardener decides to apply for the symbol, they have to agree to abide by the appropriate standards, and must pass an inspection by one of the Soil Association's qualified inspectors. Land has to be free of agrochemicals for at least two years before the producer can be awarded the Soil Association symbol, and there are also detailed criteria for the acceptability of livestock. The standards also cover environmental issues, described in detail on pages 91–4. There are also a number of 'in conversion' grades for farmers who want to be able to sell produce under a special category, before it is fully organic.

Once a producer or processor has the Soil Association symbol, they can display this on food that is made to Soil Association-approved standards. Thereafter, the producer or processor can expect to be inspected at least once a year by the Soil Association inspectors, and also to be subject to occasional spot checks to make sure that the rules are not being broken.

This is fine for produce grown in Britain, but a lot of our organic food comes from abroad. Here, the Soil Association has two main ways of tackling the problem of verification. First, for produce coming from countries where there are recognised certification schemes, the Soil Association has a number of reciprocal arrangements with foreign organisations that it accepts as being equally strict as itself in granting an organic growers symbol; for example, food imported from France and cleared by the group Nature et Progrès can be sold under the Soil Association symbol. The precise way in which this system will operate in the long term still hasn't been worked out, but will probably involve some integrated system run by the International Federation of Organic Agriculture Movements (IFOAM) based in Germany.

However, an increasing amount of produce is coming from further afield, including many isolated producers in the third world. Until these countries get their own certification programmes organised, the Soil Association will send out foreign verification inspectors anywhere in the world to ensure that products imported under the Soil Association symbol are produced to high enough standards. Recent new imports include tea and coffee from Kenya and Tanzania, more tea from Sri Lanka and honey from Zambia.

In addition, the standards are being extended to processors and non-food products, and there are plans for a special symbol scheme for retailers of organic produce. This means that products such as bread, cheese, biscuits and so on can be eligible for the symbol if they are made entirely from organic products. It also allows the symbol to be awarded to composts, natural fertilisers and other products if they fall into the criteria listed in the Soil Association standards.

Although there is still quite a lot of variation between standards in different countries, and even within countries, most keep to the same basic format as those of the Soil Association.

GOVERNMENTS GET IN ON THE GAME

Until very recently all organic standards have been managed by independent organisations, which are usually either non-profit making (like the Soil Association) or businesses, cooperatives and so on. Now governments are starting to take an active interest, and are setting standards of their own.

In Britain, since 1989, all the organic standards must adhere to the guidelines in the government's United Kingdom Register of Organic Food Standards (UKROFS). These standards are almost identical to those of the Soil Association, except that they do not, as yet, include a specific environment and conservation section (which has caused an outcry from some of the nature conservation groups in Britain, such as the Council for the Protection of Rural England). UKROFS means that all organic standards in Britain are in all fundamental respects identical; that is to say, when you buy 'organic food' it means that it should always have been grown in the same way. This might seem an obvious requirement, but getting there has taken quite a long time.

But the Soil Association symbol differs from many other eco-labels in two important respects. First, it is constantly being developed as we learn more about how the organic farming system runs, and as new environmental problems emerge or come into prominence. The standards are usually reissued in a revised form every couple of years, allowing improvements to be incorporated. For example, dipping sheep is a legal obligation in Britain, yet until recently the pesticides used in the dip were amongst the most hazardous; as soon as safer pesticides became available, the standards were revised to insist that only these were used by organic farmers.

Secondly, the standards recognise that nothing is perfect, and allow farmers some leeway, especially in the restricted category mentioned earlier. This means, for example, that if a farmer has a particular unusual pest problem, he or she can apply to the symbol committee for permission to use one of the few plant-based pesticides allowed under the standards for a number of years on one site (although this normally wouldn't be allowed). It means that if a farmer has a serious problem, they have a chance of doing something about it without opening the floodgates for anyone to use these dangerous substances. Having professional farmers and growers on the committees, who rely on organic farming for their livelihood, helps ensure that rhetoric doesn't run away with reality.

The system isn't perfect of course, and doubtless a few fraudulent traders slip through the net. But it is certainly not just a paper declaration. Symbol-holders can and do lose the symbol if they are caught breaking the rules or, more controversially, if they are inadvertently contaminated by pesticide spray drift or something similar. Recently, a large French certification programme was removed from the recognised foreign schemes because of evidence of fraud.

12
WHERE CAN I BUY ORGANIC FOOD?

According to a survey carried out by Elm Farm Research Centre in 1988, 70 per cent of consumers would buy organic food if it was more freely available. The first specialist organic shop, Wholefood, in Paddington Street, London, was founded by the then general secretary of the Soil Association, Donald Wilson, in 1960. Since then, things have changed enormously.

Fortunately, there isn't space here to list all the sources of organic food in Britain. Fortunately, because a few years ago there would have been space – all the organic food retailers would have fitted easily into a slim appendix to this handbook. Today, organic food is available at farm shops, wholefood stores, grocers, specialist shops, through mail order services and from literally hundreds of outlets of almost all the major retail chains.

This doesn't mean that organic food is in abundant supply. There is currently a higher demand than can be satisfied within Britain, so you may have trouble finding some foods, particularly during the winter months. And someone who wants to eat an entirely organic diet will have their work cut out finding the complete range of food, although it is just about possible, for supplies are increasing all the time. Listing all the suppliers now would fill up a thick volume, and would need to be constantly updated. None the less, for people wanting to buy organic food there are some general sources of information available, some of which are listed below.

SOIL ASSOCIATION REGIONAL GUIDES

The Soil Association publishes a series of regional guides that give retail sources of Soil Association symbol food, and other certified organic food throughout Britain, excluding Northern Ireland. The research for the guides is carried out by hundreds of Soil Association members, who write in with details of shops in their own area. Whilst inevitably incomplete, the regional guides are the most comprehensive guides available at present to organic food in Britain. The *Organic Food You Can Trust* series includes:

- South and East (including London)
- Wales and Borders
- Scotland and Borders
- Midlands and the North
- South West England

Some of these areas are far better stocked than others; the *Scotland and the Borders* guide is still fairly thin, for example. Top source, not surprisingly, is London, with over 40 outlets, but even a fairly small county like East Sussex has over 20 organic retail stores. The Soil Association also publishes a *Safe Meat Guide* to sources of organic additive-free and free-range meat products.

All these guides are updated regularly and include information about the types of food available from the various shops, opening hours, location and phone number. They cost £2.50 each, including postage and packing, from the Soil Association (86 Colston Street, Bristol BS1 5BB, tel. 0272 290661) and also from selected regional outlets. The Soil Association guides will continue to be updated and published in their regional format, and will also be released as a one volume book in 1991.

For retailers wanting to stock organic food, the Soil Association also produces regional lists of Soil Association symbol holders. These are printed straight off the symbol-scheme computer, and are thus completely comprehensive and up to date. They include a list of the produce available from particular farms and cost £3.00 for each region, or £12.00 for the whole of Britain, including postage and packing, from the Soil Association.

The Soil Association also produces a number of specialist lists, including:

- Inputs list of companies producing symbol-standard inputs to the organic system.
- Processors list of companies processing Soil Association symbol-standard organic produce to make biscuits, cooking oils, breakfast cereals, etc.

OTHER SOURCES OF INFORMATION

The *Thorsons Organic Consumer Guide* is published in cooperation with the Henry Doubleday Research Association, which runs the National Centre for Organic Gardening at Ryton on Dunsmore near Coventry. The book includes a number of articles about organic food and farming, plus a guide to shops selling organic produce and a section on restaurants using all or mostly organic produce.

The Born Again Carnivore by Sue Mellis and Barbara Davidson (Macdonald Optima) is a book about meat raised by non-intensive methods. It includes a detailed directory of organic and free-range supplies of meat, including most Soil Association symbol outlets, plus details about the way animals are kept, ideas for cooking meat and the arguments for humane and safe treatment of animals.

The Organic Wine Guide by Charlotte Mitchell and Iain Wright (Mainstream Publishing) gives a detailed background to the reasons for choosing organic wines, and includes a list of different wines. There are also a number of specialist organic wine mail-order services, which produce lists of different wines from all over Europe and beyond. The annual Organic Wine Fair at the National Centre for Organic Gardening is a good opportunity to see and taste organic wines.

Many sources of food, restaurants, dealers and other outlets are listed in the Soil Association's journal *Living*

Earth, which also contains a regular column, 'Food Fayre', summarising the latest information about organic foods on the market.

MAJOR RETAIL OUTLETS

Many people like to buy organic food at local shops, where they can get to know the shopkeepers and perhaps build up regular orders. An increasing number of organic farms now run their own shops. However, for people without access to these, many of the larger retail chains, including Safeways, Sainsburys and Tescos, are stocking organic vegetables, fruit, dairy produce and meat at an increasing number of their stores. For example, Safeways are now stocking organic food at all 314 of their stores around the country. Marks & Spencer, which withdrew from organic produce at the end of 1990, are reconsidering and will probably start stocking selected produce again.

If you can avoid it, never buy organic food unless it has a recognised symbol that guarantees that it comes from a genuine organic source. There is certainly some fraudulent organic produce reaching retail outlets. And if you find shops that are not mentioned in our guides (or you run one yourself), please let us know at the Soil Association, as we are anxious to keep up to date with new sources of organic food as they appear.

13
CAN I GROW ORGANIC FOOD FOR MYSELF?

So far we have looked at the reasons for eating organic food; what organic farming really means in practice; and how to go about buying organic food. This just leaves us with the last step, although for many readers this will be the most important step of all: Can anyone grow organic food? The answer is a definite 'yes'. Anyone with a garden, allotment or just a couple of window boxes in a flat can grow organic food to eat.

This book doesn't try to provide you with a complete introduction to organic gardening. There are already dozens of excellent guides available, and some of the best are listed in the section on page 150. Instead, we explain why organic gardening is so fundamentally different from gardening with sprays and artificial fertilisers, and we provide some practical ideas on how to get started.

WHAT IS ORGANIC GARDENING?

Organic gardening is based on a wholly different approach to the mainstream style of growing food (and flowers and lawns). You can't just take a few ideas from organic gardening, tack them on to a conventional garden, and hope to be gardening organically, although some of the elements of organic gardening are used by almost all gardeners, whether they call themselves organic or not. Having said that, you shouldn't be put off by thinking that organic gardening is something difficult, semi-mystical or particularly extreme. Most of what follows is just good commonsense.

We could say that organic agriculture makes more use of a knowledge of ecology than of chemistry. The International Federation of Organic Agriculture Movements (IFOAM) describes this more elegantly when it says that organic farming should 'work with natural systems rather than seeking to dominate them' and should 'encourage and enhance biological cycles within the farming system, involving micro-organisms, soil flora and fauna, plants and animals'. However, this doesn't mean just popping a few food plants in amongst an entirely wild area, although there are some growing systems that almost go as far as this, including the 'one-straw revolution' method, which is popular in Japan, and to a lesser extent permaculture, a popular growing method pioneered in Australia. Organic farming and gardening is a far more artificial system than either of these; it tries to produce food efficiently, and in sufficient quantities, without totally upsetting the balance of nature. And it does this by using methods that manage to retain some of the best aspects of a natural system.

Take the rotation, for example; the rotation is a system whereby different crops are grown on a plot of land each year, on a regular cycle, to ensure that the soil stays in balance and to break the life cycles of pests and diseases. Farm rotations have already been described on page 72, and garden rotations will be looked at below. The rotation is completely unnatural. It is highly unlikely that one plot of land would have entirely different plants growing on it each year, with no trace of last year's species. But although rotations are unnatural, they mimic the natural cycle by ensuring that any one piece of the farm or garden has a variety of crops over time, rather than the year-in, year-out monocultures found on many intensive chemical farms. This practice, of imitating the best aspects of the natural system, runs right through the philosophy of organic gardening.

As an organic gardener you will have to consider a

number of different things, all of which are important in maintaining a productive, balanced garden:
- The soil.
- The crops, and when they are grown.
- Other plants and animals in the garden (including weeds and pests).

THE LIVING SOIL

The soil is the basis upon which all other aspects of organic gardening rely. As we have seen earlier, the links between soil-plant-animal and ourselves have an importance that extends way outside the confines of the farm or garden. Keeping soil alive, strong and in good condition is the most important skill involved in organic gardening. This means:
- Keeping a good structure, so that the soil allows plants to grow correctly, does not blow or wash away, and can hold moisture and nutrients.
- Ensuring that the soil stays fertile, with enough nutrients, trace elements, the correct pH (i.e. balance of acidity and alkalinity) and useful bacteria, fungi and other creatures.
- In turn this means making sure it is really living soil, with a balanced plant and animal ecology of its own.

It also means learning to recognise when soil is not as healthy as it should be, and knowing what to do about it.

How do I know what state the soil is in?

Before you start, it is worth making a stab at finding out about the state of the soil. For the commercial farmer and gardener it may well be worth paying for a proper soil analysis, but for home gardeners the expense won't be worthwhile. Instead, you can buy some very simple soil-testing kits, to measure pH (acidity/alkalinity); very acidic soil will not grow many plants, and lime or other calcareous material may have to be added to make it more suitable.

Even more important, you can simply use your eyes to

Plants as indicators of soil conditions

Common name	Latin name	Heavy	Light	Acidic	Alkaline	Wet
Bindweed	Calystegia spp.					✓
Bracken	Pteridium aquilinum		✓	✓		
Burnett, salad	Sanguisorba minor				✓	✓
Buttercup, creeping	Ranunculus repens				✓	
Campion, bladder	Silene vulgaris					
Campion, white	Silene alba					
Clover	Trifolium spp.					
Coltsfoot	Tussilago farfara	✓	✓	✓		✓
Cornflower	Centaurea cyanus					
Corn marigold	Chrysanthemum segetum	✓✓	✓✓	✓		
Daisy	Bellis perennis					
Dandelion	Taraxacum spp.					
Dock, broad-leaved	Rumex obtusifolius	✓	✓✓			✓
Horsetail	Equisetum spp.					
Mayweed, scentless	Triplospermum inodorum					
Nettle, small	Urtica urens				✓	
Pimpernel, scarlet	Anagillis arvensis					
Plantain	Plantago spp.	✓	✓			
Redshank	Polygonum persecaria			✓✓✓		✓✓
Shepherd's purse	Capsella bursa-pastoris					
Silverweed	Potentilla anserina		✓			
Sorrel, common	Rumex acetosa					
Sorrel, sheep's	Rumex acetosalla					
Spurrey	Spergula spp.					
Sow thistle	Cicerbita spp.					

129

see what is growing there already. Many weed species have become adapted to grow in soil lacking certain nutrients; indeed, most 'weeds' are tough survivors amongst the plant kingdom, and many grow in places where other plants cannot survive. By identifying the wild plants that spring up as weeds, you can help find out what nutrients are missing, or in excess, in your garden, as the accompanying table shows. Note that these are only indications of soil conditions; the weeds you get in your garden depend a lot on what seeds have been introduced by chance, and any one garden might have many plants that 'indicate' completely different things. But plant indicators are especially important when one particular species has become dominant.

The next move is to dig around in the soil. If you find a rich soil life, and especially a lot of earthworms, this is a good sign that the soil hasn't been too badly damaged. You can also see if there are many worms about by looking for their casts on the lawn, and by searching for them by torchlight on warm wet summer nights.

Once you have an idea of the state of your soil, you have to go about improving, or maintaining, its fertility.

IMPROVING SOIL FERTILITY

The most important way of maintaining, or improving, soil fertility is by replacing the nutrients that have been lost from the soil when crops or flowers are removed. In a chemical garden this is done mainly by using soluble fertilisers, manufactured from raw materials or, in the case of nitrogen, collected from the atmosphere in an expensive and high-energy process.

In an organic garden you will be working as much as possible within a closed system, which means recycling waste plant material through composting and other methods. In practice, complete recycling isn't usually possible in a small garden, so other materials are brought in as organic fertilisers; virtually anything that has been living can be returned to the soil, although the scope for the back gardener is usually much narrower. First and foremost, of course, is the compost heap.

Why make compost?

Compost is organic material that has been collected together and provided with the best conditions to allow it to break down, or decompose, as quickly as possible. Composting is a vital tool for the organic gardener, for two reasons:

- Material breaks down much more quickly than if it were simply left on the soil surface (as happens in natural situations), so that it quickly releases nutrients for plants to use.

- Heat generated by the bacteria carrying out the decomposition raises the temperature in the centre of the compost heap to a high enough level so that weed seeds, and other harmful pathogens, are usually killed by the composting process.

Gourmet compost-making

Making compost is easy, but there are a few simple things to bear in mind if you want to make the quickest, best and most useful compost.

The bacteria that carry out the composting process work best (i.e. grow and reproduce as quickly as possible) in warm, moist conditions with plenty of oxygen. Most gardeners make compost in an aerated covered box to get these optimum conditions. There are many special compost bins on the market, made of wood or plastic; some of these are not bad, and a few may even work quite well, but there are many shoddily made, over-elaborate or just plain bad designs on the market. When the Centre for Alternative Technology in Wales carried out tests on a range of commercial compost bins a few years ago the gardeners found that many fell to bits within two or three years. You are almost certainly safest buying a strong wooden box or, even better, making one yourself; plans for the famous New Zealand compost bin are given in the accompanying diagram.

If you want to make compost as quickly as possible, it's best to collect materials together and construct the heap all in one go. For the best compost, the constituents should

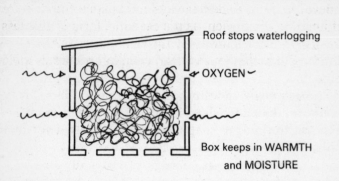

Roof stops waterlogging

OXYGEN

Box keeps in WARMTH
and MOISTURE

- The bacteria that make compost need warm, moist conditions with plenty of oxygen to work best. A ratio of carbon:nitrogen of 30:1 is needed for the best breakdown.
- Most gardeners make compost in an aerated, covered box to get these optimum conditions, but some of the best compost is made in simple heaps. (Several methods are described in the poster on 'Compost' in section 4.)
- Compost can be made very simply by leaving plant matter to rot in a heap and turning it over every few months. This will never reach a high enough temperature to kill weed seeds but may be easier for the person with a small garden. Care must be taken that oxygen can get into the heap, or else a different type of bacteria will come in (anaerobic bacteria) and the compost will smell very strongly.
- It is important to have a draught underneath the box as well.

Compost bin plan

contain a ratio of carbon to nitrogen of about 30:1. As plant material contains mainly carbon and not much nitrogen, this means that using a little animal manure or urine in a compost heap will often make it work better. Indeed, some gardeners always compost manure before adding it to the garden, as it's then in a form that is less likely to be leached away by the rain and lost. As well as plant waste and manures, good compost materials include urine, fish waste, bones, seaweed, sawdust and twigs, while other materials that can be composted but that shouldn't make up more than 10 per cent of the total heap, include undyed paper, ash, wool and leaves (for composting large amounts of leaves see below).

Compost material	Carbon	Nitrogen	Phosphate
ANIMAL			
Manure (mammal)		●	
Manure (chicken)		●	●
Dried blood		●	
Urine		●	
Fish waste		●	●
Bones			●
MIXTURE			
Farmyard manure and straw	●	●	
PLANT			
Bracken	●	·	
Garden weeds	●	·	
Lawn clippings		·	
Seaweed	·	●	
Peat	·	·	
Straw	●	·	
Wood (sawdust, paper, twigs)	●		
Legumes	·	●	
Comfrey		●	

Composition of compost material (the larger the circle, the more of the nutrient)

Don't ignore your weeds when building a compost heap. Some plants tend to concentrate nutrients, so weed species can be a valuable constituent of compost; for example chickweeds concentrate manganese and phosphorus, goosegrass concentrates calcium, and silverweed concentrates calcium, iron and magnesium. But try to pick weeds for the heap before they go to seed; if they have seeds, either remove them or throw the plants into the centre of the heap, where it will get hottest.

Nettles are extremely rich in nitrate and make a very good compost material; indeed, some gardeners collect piles of nettles and soak them in water for about a month to make liquid manure, to be used on plants, such as tomatoes, celery and marrow, that need continuous heavy feeding. Comfrey, which is also rich in potassium, can be treated in the same way; the mix suggested by the Henry Doubleday Research Association is 14 lb of comfrey to 20 gallons of water. Liquid manures are probably best used on potted plants or in greenhouses, simply because they are extremely likely to leach away if used outside. They should be applied with a watering can, avoiding direct contact with stems and foliage if possible. Generally, compost is a much better material to use.

Once you've collected together the compost materials they should be made into a loose heap. Anything tough or woody should be broken up with a shovel, and put in the centre of the heap. Many gardeners buy an activator to make sure the heap breaks down quickly; however, most activators are chemically very similar to urine, and it's probably cheaper, and more effective, to make judicious use of a 'pee can', although many people balk at the prospect.

Turn the compost heap every few weeks. If the weather is cool, try putting an old carpet on top of the heap to help build up the heat. You should be able to feel the heat rising to the surface after a few days, and see the whole heap steaming; temperatures of over 75°C are by no means uncommon.

A good compost heap works very quickly. You can

expect to get ready-to-use compost in two or three weeks in the summer, but only if you build a proper compost box and take some time making and tending the heap. Simply leaving plant and kitchen waste in a pile, and turning it over every so often with a fork, will also make compost, but this will probably take a few months and won't get hot enough to kill the weed seeds off. It's up to you.

Once the compost is made, you can either fork it into the soil or spread it over the surface in a mulch, as described below. Forking in is best done in the winter, when the garden is resting, but compost can be added at any stage.

OTHER WAYS OF IMPROVING SOIL FERTILITY

You don't have to stop with compost. We have already looked briefly at liquid manures in the section above. The organic gardener can also use several other fertility-building techniques, including:

- Mulching.
- Leafmould.
- Green manuring.
- Rotations.

Mulching

Mulching means covering the soil surface with organic materials, rather than digging them into the soil. These materials can include not only manures and composts, but also lawn cuttings, leaves, straw, tea leaves, coffee grounds and paper. Indeed, if materials with low nitrogen content are to be added, they are best used as a mulch because otherwise they may deplete the soil of nitrogen as they break down (called nitrogen robbery).

In theory, mulching is an excellent option because it helps keep the soil warm and moist, suppresses weed growth and can help replace digging and hoeing. Worms and other soil dwellers gradually pull the material down into the soil in a closer simulation of a natural system. Unfortunately, the mulch can also provide ideal cover for

a range of pests, including the notorious slug. You just
have to try it out; if pests start to build up it may not be
the best method for you.

Leafmould

Leafmould is a way of making use of (and also getting rid
of) masses of fallen leaves. Leaves from most trees take at
least two years to break down enough to be useful to the
gardener, but then make an excellent compost or mulch. If
you have a large enough garden or allotment, three leaf
mould bins, made of wood or wire netting, can be used on a
tri-annual cycle, so that you always have excellent mulch
ready to use each year, and the bin is filled in the autumn
for use again in three years time.

Green manuring

Green manuring, which we have discussed briefly in the
farming chapter (see page 88), is again only really
applicable to someone with a larger garden or allotment.
Green manures are crops that are planted especially to be
dug back into the soil to increase organic matter, to
improve poor soil by concentrating certain nutrients, and
to help reduce leaching of nutrients. Popular green
manures include:

- Hungarian rye, used for winter cover.
- Annual lupin, which is a legume and thus fixes
  nitrogen from the air, as well as concentrating
  phosphate.
- Clovers, which are also legumes.
- Buckwheat, which is useful in helping to break up
  heavy clay soils, and is also a good way of attracting
  the beneficial hoverfly, as described on page 142).
- Mustard, which is said to protect potatoes against
  wireworm if planted previously.
- Kale, which is a useful winter cover, added to which
  the leaves can also be eaten.

Green manuring is certainly worthwhile if you are starting
a new garden from scratch and need to improve the soil,
especially in a situation where you have just moved into a

new house and don't really have the time to start gardening in earnest. The cost of the seeds will be repaid with a carpet of green for a while and will help build up valuable humus in the soil. It may also be worth thinking about if you have bare soil over the winter, or want to give a particular bed a bit of a nutrient or humus boost.

Rotations

Rotations are so important that they need a section to themselves.

Rotations are intrinsic to the organic method. They play an important role both in helping to maintain a healthy soil and in controlling pests. Soil will maintain its fertility better if different crops are grown in a particular bed in different years; this is because each species needs specific types and concentrations of nutrients, and by rotating species the soil has the chance to build these up again. In addition, the rotation helps break the life cycle of some of the most important garden pests. The heavy use of pesticides on many commercial market gardens is because the same crops are planted in the same beds every year.

There are no hard and fast rules about rotations, except that virtually all rotations contain some legumes (pea and bean family) because these help restore nitrogen levels in the soil. Whatever system you adopt, you don't have to follow it slavishly year after year; a range of options can be used in any bed, for example:

A typical rotation
Year 1   Brassica and compost
Year 2   Legumes and lime
Year 3   Potatoes and manure, followed by green
         manure
Year 4   Roots
Year 5   Back to brassicas again
         And so on

or . . .

Year 1   Lettuce/spinach/cabbage/radish
Year 2   Runner, dwarf and French beans/peas/onions
Year 3   Carrots/beetroots/potatoes

Or again:

Year 1   Legumes
Year 2   Anything else

Or another possibility:

Year 1   Potatoes
Year 2   Roots
Year 3   Miscellaneous
Year 4   Legumes and brassicas

The rotation needs some basic commonsense to function
properly. Potatoes and brassicas are the hungriest crops,
so they need some compost and manures to help them
along. Peas and beans need less feeding and, as we've
seen, should leave some nutrients behind. Root crops need
compost if they follow potatoes (and it should be compost
because carrots and parsnips don't like manure). Some
crops, such as many salad crops, are fast growing and
adaptable, and can thus be fitted into the rotation
wherever most suitable.

You will notice that, unlike the farming rotation
described on page 00, the garden rotations don't usually
include a fallow period; this is because most gardeners do
not have the space for this. But, it is an excellent help to
the garden if you do have space to leave one bed fallow
every year.

One important point, which it is easy to forget. You
should keep a record of your rotations. A sturdy notebook
in the garden shed, ideally including a plan of the garden
with the beds numbered, makes sure that the rotation
isn't forgotten and confused over the four or five year
period. A well loved garden notebook is also one of the
organic gardeners most valuable possessions and can be
used to note down incidence of disease and pests,
combinations of crops that seem to work well in a

particular garden environment, details about the soil, and so on. Once you've grasped the basics, personal experience is often far more useful than a whole bookcase full of other people's knowledge.

CONTROLLING PESTS AND DISEASES IN THE ORGANIC GARDEN

Pests and diseases are plants and animals that live in places where we don't want them, and eat the things that we want to eat ourselves. Although organic gardeners try to maintain as much of a balance of nature in their gardens as possible, the fact that you are growing dense stands of particular plants, which you want to be in good enough condition to eat, means that you will probably have to help nature along a bit in its efforts to control unwanted pests.

Organic gardeners do not use artificial pesticides. They do use a few plant-based pesticides, as we will see below, but usually only in an emergency, as a last resort. None the less, there are a whole barrage of alternative pest control methods available. Not all of them will work for you, and some of the old folk remedies are frankly fairly dubious at the best of times. But others are excellent and efficient ways of controlling pests without recourse to pesticides.

The most important step in controlling pests and, especially, diseases is to keep your garden healthy, with a healthy soil. Spending time on soil fertility, and building up a living soil is also an important part of pest control. Once you've done this, plants will be a lot less susceptible to disease attack. However, if you do suffer from pest and disease outbreaks (which you inevitably will at some time), there are a number of things you can do.

A couple of the best known methods of pest control have already been described; rotations and mulches are both ways of preventing pests by stopping them building up in the soil and, in the latter case, preventing weeds from growing by putting a physical barrier in their way. Other organic pest control methods fall into a number of different categories:

- Biological control, by both encouraging natural predators and by introducing specific biological control organisms.
- Planting times can be staggered to avoid pests of specific crops.
- Keeping plants healthy.
- Disguising plants.
- Erecting barriers.
- Setting traps to catch and/or kill pests.
- Manual weeding and pest control.
- Use of approved pesticides.

Biological pest control

Biological control is the most important of these steps for the organic gardener, as it is for the organic farmer. Leaving some areas of the garden wild encourages useful animals (but also shelters pests); helping useful animals by feeding them in winter, providing breeding sites and growing plants that attract them can all help build up healthy populations. Some examples are listed below.

Birds are almost always useful. Robins eat many soil pests, tits eat large numbers of insect pests, and blackbirds and thrushes will mop up prodigious quantities of snails and small slugs. All these birds will benefit if they are fed during the lean parts of the winter, and many will stay in your garden if you provide nest boxes.

Hedgehogs are especially useful for hunting slugs and snails. They need some wild space nearby to live in, and will sometimes become very tame, making regular visits for a saucer of milk. Like birds, hedgehogs can sometimes be attracted by giving them a good home to breed in.

Frogs and, especially, toads are ace slug hunters. They will stay in gardens if there is a damp area or, ideally, a pond that they can get into and out of easily. Frogs can be encouraged by adding some frogspawn to a garden pond. Toads usually always return to the place where they were born, but sometimes breed in a new site and will happily

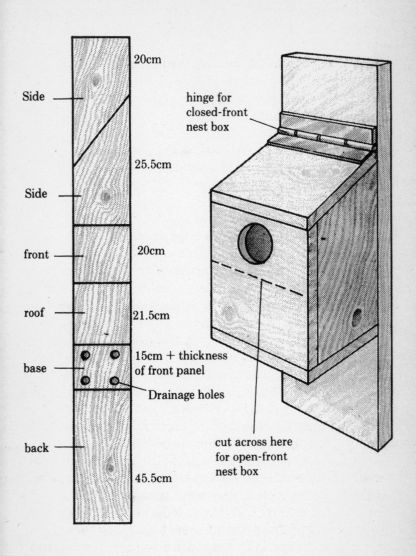

Side

Side

front

roof

base

back

20cm

25.5cm

20cm

21.5cm

15cm + thickness
of front panel

Drainage holes

45.5cm

hinge for
closed-front
nest box

cut across here
for open-front
nest box

Plans for a nest box

take up residence in a garden pond for the rest of the year.

Hoverflies are useful because their larvae have been measured as eating up to 120 aphids in an hour. They are attracted by buckwheat.

Ladybird and Lacewing larvae are also very gluttonous aphid eaters, and should be encouraged wherever possible.

It should go without saying by now that any spraying or pesticide use will tend to kill off your friends as well as your enemies. A particular danger point is the use of slug pellets, which can easily kill hedgehogs and small birds. Even if the pellets are kept away from the animals themselves, dead slugs containing lethal doses of poison can still be eaten. Spraying aphids will not do you any good at all if you also kill the insects that feed on them all the time; aphids breed extremely quickly and will replace their numbers far faster than their predators.

Judicious use of planting times
Planting times and methods can also be used to confuse or discourage pests; for example, sowing either very early or very late varieties of beans can avoid the blackfly (*Aphis fabae*) that is found in the spring. Using onion sets, to avoid the vulnerable period when the seeds and seedlings are particularly susceptible to disease, can help cut out damage from the onion root fly (*Delia antiqua*).

Keep plants healthy
Keeping plants healthy might seem a self evident requirement, but it is worth stressing. The philosophy that states that one bad apple can spoil the barrel applies to the garden as well, and the organic gardener must be especially alert to remove sick or dead specimens before they fall prey to other diseases that may spread to previously healthy individuals. You should remove any parts of a plant that looked diseased, and remove the whole plant if it is one of a group. These remains should be burnt or disposed of in a sealed plastic bag, and certainly not added to the compost heap.

Disguising plants

Many organic gardeners swear that intercropping food plants with strong smelling plants helps disguise them and, literally, throws pest species off the scent. There has been little quantifiable research into this, and there must be some doubts about the success of such methods, given the extreme sensitivity of many insects to particular important smells, but for anyone who wants to try, the accompanying table lists some useful scented herbs.

Garden pests and the scented plants they are confused by

Pest	Scented plant
Aphids	Nasturtiums
Ants	Pennyroyal, spearmint
Cabbage moth	Sage, mint
Cabbage white butterfly	Sage, rosemary, hyssop, thyme, mint, celery, peppermint
Carrot fly	Onions, leeks, rosemary, sage, salsify, dried herbs when planting
Flea beetle	Wormwood, mint
Flies and mosquitoes	Basil
Whitefly	Nasturtiums
General deterrents	Marigolds, onion, tansy, wormwood, henbit, geranium, asters

Barriers to pests

Erecting barriers certainly works with some pests. For example, grease bands painted on the lower stems of fruit trees can help stop pests which climb up from the ground. The cabbage root fly (*Delia brassica*) can be blocked from its habit of attacking the roots of cabbages by pushing the young cabbage root through a 5 mm hole in a 20-centimetre-square patch of roofing felt; the cabbage grows to fit the hole tightly, and the felt is pushed flat against the soil, leaving no room for the fly to crawl underneath. Once in position, it can remain an effective barrier for the whole growing season.

Other barriers that you may hear a lot about don't seem to work very well in practice. For example, there are numerous barriers suggested for slugs, including sprinkling hard sand and charcoal around the edges of beds, but this never actually seems to stop many slugs.

Traps
Setting traps can work in specific cases. Some people find a saucer of stale beer is an excellent trap for slugs, which crawl inside and either drown or can be picked out and killed. However, other people have little luck with this method.

A tin can filled with vegetable scraps and punched through with small holes can be buried in the vegetable bed and checked regularly for millipedes, wireworms and other pests. There are many other traps listed in some of the recommended books, but all tend to be fairly labour intensive.

Weeding
Manual weeding is still the way that most gardeners get rid of weeds in both vegetable patches and flower beds. Unless you care about having an ultra-neat appearance, weeding doesn't have to be compulsive so long as the weeds don't start to swamp your crops. It is obviously best to pull them out before they set seed.

A form of manual weeding is also one of the best ways of getting rid of the gardener's most implacable foes – slugs and snails. Half an hour with a torch on a wet night can result in a huge haul in a garden where they are a problem. Once you've got them, you then have the ethical choice of either taking them a long way away into a piece of waste land and leaving them to carry out their natural lives, or of killing them. Despite what people say about the effectiveness of dropping slugs and snails into salted water, this is a slow and miserable death. The only quick way to kill molluscs in the garden is by stamping on them or squashing them under a stone, unpleasant as either of these options may be.

Approved pesticides

Approved pesticides are still available for the organic gardener in emergencies, with the stress on emergencies; always remember that using such pesticides will inevitably kill off some of the beneficial insects as well. The pesticides that are approved by the Soil Association standards, and available for gardeners, are:

- Pyrethrum, made from flowers of *Chrysanthemum folium*, a Kenyan species. It has a quick paralysing effect on insects, but only remains poisonous for a short time. Always spray on cloudy days if possible, so that you minimise deaths amongst bees and other nectar-feeding insects including butterflies.
- Derris is a stronger and more persistent pesticide, manufactured from rotenone. Like pyrethrum, it is not harmful to mammals and birds, and is not concentrated in the food chain.
- Quassia chips are wood chips from the tropical quassia tree, which can be boiled up in water to make a solution that kills aphids and other pests.

There are also a number of commercially marketed spores of bacteria that attack certain pest species and are used especially in greenhouses.

COMPANION PLANTING

One popular idea amongst organic gardeners is companion planting – planting particular species together that are mutually beneficial. Despite the amount written about companion planting, we still don't know very much about how it works, and some organic gardeners don't really believe that it works at all. Certainly, plants can help by attracting particular beneficial insects, but more complex symbiotic (i.e. mutually beneficial) interactions have not been well studied in garden plants.

The chart lists some combinations that are claimed to be either helpful or harmful. It certainly shouldn't be taken as definitive, but it may be of interest to gardeners to try out some of the combinations for themselves and see how they do work in practice.

CROP SPECIES \ EFFECTOR SPECIES	ASPARAGUS	BEANS	BEANS (BROAD)	BEANS (DWARF)	BEETS	CABBAGE	CARROTS	CORN	CUCUMBER	CELERY	GARLIC	KOHL-RABI	LEEK	LETTUCE	OATS	ONIONS	PEAS	POTATOES	RADISHES	STRAWBERRY	SWEETCORN	TOMATOES
ASPARAGUS																						●
BEANS					■	●	●		●		■	■	●			■		●				
BEANS (BROAD)									●									●				
BEANS (DWARF)								●														
BEETS		■		●						●						●						
CABBAGE	●			●												●		●		■		■
CARROTS													●	●		●	●					
CORN		●							●							●	●					
CUCUMBER		●		●			●	●								●	■		●			
CELERY			●		●								●									●
GARLIC		■		●	●									●		●						●
KOHL-RABI		■		●														■				
LEEK						●				●						●						
LETTUCE						●	●												●	●		
OATS		●				●																
ONIONS		■		●	●					●		●		●			●			●		●
PEAS		●	●				●	●	●		■					■		■	●		●	
POTATOES		●	●			●	●	●	■													
RADISHES	●								●					●			●					●
STRAWBERRY		●	●	●	■																	
SWEETCORN																	●					
TOMATOES	●					●	●			●	■					●		■				

● helpful interaction   ■ harmful interaction

Some examples of combination planting

WHERE TO GARDEN

Many people are lucky enough to have gardens or
allotments big enough to grow some of their food. If you
count in your labour, it won't save you any money.
However, working a garden isn't quite as much effort as
many people make out, especially when you get the hang
of what grows best in your area and in your own plot of
land. (Try talking to neighbouring gardeners for advice
about crops and varieties.) And, of course, it is a healthy
pastime that allows you to have access to home-grown
fresh organic produce you really can guarantee.

Even for people without big gardens, it is possible to
grow a proportion of vegetables in a backyard or even in a
window box; there are several books available about
gardening in small spaces and even indoors. Alternatively,
you can try to borrow a neighbour's garden, if they are
either uninterested or unable to garden it themselves,
perhaps paying rent with a few vegetables. Some years
ago, local groups of Friends of the Earth started several
successful garden-share schemes.

But a word of warning. Even nowadays, when lead-free
fuel is becoming more available, there are large amounts of
lead found near busy roads and in inner city areas. If your
garden or plot backs on to a major road, or you think that
it could be contaminated by lead and other vehicle
pollutants, it would be worth having a soil test carried out
before you start.

AFTERWORD:
A CELEBRATION OF GOOD FOOD AND FARMING

This book has given a brief introduction to the work of the Soil Association, and the organic movement, in Britain. At a time of food scares, political upheavals in agriculture, and extravagant claims and counter claims, it is sometimes easy to lose sight of the reason for doing the work that we do.

We're very lucky in Britain to have enough to eat. But some of the things that have been done to achieve our abundant supply of food are damaging – to our own environment, to people living in poorer countries, and to our own health. We now have a real chance to address some of these problems, in part through adopting the principles of organic agriculture.

The Soil Association is unlike most other groups in the environment, food and farming movements because it is based around a positive message. When we suggest, or demand, that something damaging be stopped, we do so from the perspective of having a worked-out alternative. Although we've stressed the differences between organic and conventional husbandry in this book, there are a lot of similarities as well. Organic agriculture isn't something that requires a total change of lifestyle; it's proponents are neither romantics nor idealogues. Organic agriculture has only progressed as far as it has because it works. The task of the Soil Association now is to see that it continues to progress towards and into the next century.

It is also worth remembering that the Soil Association is not just about prosaic things such as pollution control and removal of contaminants in food. It is also about a celebration of the best things in food, and in life; about food that tastes good instead of just looking good; about food that has variety. It is a tragedy, for example, that almost all the hundreds of varieties of fruit that were available in the 1960s now cannot be sold legally under the terms of the EC Common Agricultural Policy. We have suffered a loss of choice as well as a loss of quality. Organic food and farming seeks to recover the best of the past in this respect, without losing sight of the needs of the present, or of the genuinely helpful innovations in agriculture that have occurred since the Second World War. This is why a growing number of chefs, food writers and gourmets are turning over to organic food. We hope that this book has helped stimulate your own taste for a method which protects human health and the environment.

If so, and if you would like to know more about the Soil Association, please write to us for more information, enclosing a stamped addressed envelope. Better still, join us, using the form reprinted at the back of this book, or just by writing in. You will have the chance to join one of our 40 local groups, you will get a quarterly magazine, plus other mailings, and access to our mail-order book services, campaigns and activities. Best of all, you will be helping us to carry on our work. We rely on your support.

FURTHER
INFORMATION

The Soil Association is at 86 Colston Street,
Bristol BS1 5BB. Telephone 0272 290661

The Association publishes *The Living Earth* and *Soil
Association News* six times a year, priced £2.50 or free to
members. In addition, they provide a mail order book
service covering around 200 titles relating to the organic
movement. A book catalogue is available on request. This
includes the full range of Soil Association publications.

RECOMMENDED SOIL ASSOCIATION PUBLICATIONS

Regional Guides, £2.00 each

Provides up-to-date information on outlets for organic
produce in the following regions: Scotland and Borders,
Wales and Borders, Midlands and North, West Country,
South and East (including London).

Safe Meat List
Nigel Dudley, Mandy Pullen and Sue Stolton. £2.00.

The Directory of the Organic Movement
£1.50.

The Living Earth
£2.50 (free to members).

Standards for Organic Agriculture
British Organic Standards Committee. £6.50.

Gardening Without Chemicals
Roy Lacey. £1.00.

How Does Your Garden Grow
Nigel Dudley. £1.00.

Guidelines for Conservation
Soil Association Symbol Committee. £2.00.

ADDITIONAL RECOMMENDED READING

Collected Papers on Organic Farming
Edited by Nicolas Lampkin, Centre for Organic
Husbandry and Agroecology. Aberystwyth University
Press, £5.00.

Converting to Organic Farming
Edited by Nicolas Lampkin. Elm Farm Research Centre
publications, £5.00.

The Living Soil and the Haughley Experiment
Lady Eve Balfour. Universe Books, (currently out of print
but copies available from the Soil Association) £4.00.

Organic Farming
Nicolas Lampkin. Farming Press, £19.95.

Organic Farming, An Option for the 90's
British Organic Farmers and Organic Growers Association,
£2.50.

Organic Gardening
Lawrence Hills. Penguin Books, £4.99.

Nutrition and Health
Sir R. McCarrison. McCarrison Society, £4.95.

Nitrates
Nigel Dudley. Green Print, £4.99.

The Organic Tradition
Edited by Philip Cornford. Green Books, £6.50.

This Poisoned Earth
Nigel Dudley. Piatkus, £3.99.

Small is Possible
George McRobie. Abacus, £3.50.

Small is Beautiful
E.F. Schumacher. Abacus, £4.50.

USEFUL
ADDRESSES

Please enclose a large, stamped addressed envelope with
any enquiries.

Bio Dynamic Agricultural Association
Woodman Lane,
Clent,
Stourbridge,
West Midlands DY9 9PX.
Tel: 0562 884933

**British Association of Homoeopathic Veterinary
Surgeons**
c/o Chris Day,
Secretary,
Chinham House,
Stanford in the Vale,
Faringdon,
Oxon SN7 8NQ.
Tel: 03677 324

British Organic Farmers
86 Colston Street,
Bristol BS1 5BB.
Tel: 0272 299666

British Organic Standards Committee
Elm Farm Research Centre,
Hamstead Marshall,
Newbury,
Berks RG15 0HR.
Tel: 0488 58298

Compassion in World Farming
20 Lavant Street,
Petersfield,
Hants GU32 3EW.
Tel: 0730 64208

Earthworks
12 Mason Close,
Malvern,
Worcs WR14 2NF.
Tel: 0905 22179

Earth Resources Research Ltd
258 Pentonville Road,
London N1 9JY.
Tel: 071 278 3833

Elm Farm Research Centre
(Progressive Farming Trust Ltd)
Hamstead Marshall,
Newbury,
Berks RG15 0HR.
Tel: 0488 58298

Food Commission
88 Old Street,
London EC1V 9AR.
Tel: 071 253 9513

Henry Doubleday Research Association
National Centre for Organic Gardening,
Ryton on Dunsmore,
Coventry CV8 3LG.
Tel: 0203 303517

Humane Slaughter Association
34 Blanche Lane,
South Mimms,
Potters Bar,
Herts EN6 3PA.
Tel: 0707 59040

Intermediate Technology Development Group
Myson House,
Railway Terrace,
Rugby CV21 3HT.
Tel: 0788 60631

Irish Organic Farmers' and Growers' Association
14 Berkeley Road,
Dublin 7,
Eire.
Tel: 0001 30 7996

Land Heritage
Wellington,
Somerset.
Tel: 0823 667764

McCarrison Society for Nutrition in Health
24 Paddington Street,
London W1M 4DR.
Tel: 071 935 3924

National Federation of City Farms
The Old Vicarage,
66 Fraser Street,
Windmill Hill,
Bedminster,
Bristol BS3 4LY.
Tel: 0272 660663

New Farmer and Grower
86 Colston Street,
Bristol BS1 5BB.
Tel: 0272 299666/299800

Organic Advisory Service
Elm Farm Research Centre,
Hamstead Marshall,
Newbury,
Berks RG15 0HR.
Tel: 0488 58298

Organic Growers' Association
86 Colston Street,
Bristol BS1 5BB.
Tel: 0272 299800

Organic Living Association
St Mary's Villa,
Hanley Swan,
Worcs WR8 0EA.

Parents for Safe Food
Britannica House,
1–11 Glenthorne Road,
London W6 0LF.
Tel: 081 748 9898 x 330

Permaculture Association
8 Hunters Moon,
Dartington,
Totnes,
Devon TQ9 6JT.
Tel: 0803 867546 or 0568 4041

Pesticides Trust
20 Compton Terrace,
London N1 2UN.
Tel: 071 354 3860

Royal Society for Nature Conservation
The Green,
Nettleham,
Lincoln LN2 2NR.
Tel: 0522 752326

Royal Society for the Protection of Birds
The Lodge,
Sandy,
Beds SC19 2DL.
Tel: 0767 80551

Sustainability Ltd
49 Princes Street,
London N11 4QA.
Tel: 071 243 1277

WWOOF
(Working Weekends on Organic Farms)
19 Bradford Road,
Lewes,
East Sussex BN7 1RB.

OVERSEAS ORGANISATIONS

TOOL
(Technical Development with Developing Countries)
Stichting TOOL,
Entrepotdok 68a/69a,
1018 AD Amsterdam,
Netherlands.
Tel: 020-264409

Ecological Agriculture
Agricultural University,
Haarweg 333/NL 6709 RZ,
Wageningen,
Netherlands.
Tel: 0 88370 83522

IFOAM
(International Federation of Organic Agricultural
Movements)
c/o Oekozentrum Imsbach,
D 6695 Tholey-Theley,
West Germany.

Natural Food Associates
PO Box 210,
Atlanta,
Texas 210,
USA.

Soil Association of South Australia Inc
GPO Box 2497,
Adelaide,
South Australia 5001.

Soil Association of South Africa
PO Box 47100,
Parklands,
2121 South Africa.

More books from Optima

OPTIMA HANDBOOKS

Amnesty International Handbook compiled by **Amnesty International British Section**
ISBN 0 356 18840 X, price (in UK only) £4.99, printed on recycled paper.

Friends of the Earth Handbook edited by **Jonathon Porritt**
ISBN 0 356 19108 7, price (in UK only) £5.99, printed on recycled paper.
'... compiled by the staff and supporters of Friends of the Earth and contains all the practical advice you need to become a good environmentalist.' *The Guardian*

The WWF Environment Handbook by **Mark Carwardine**
ISBN 0 356 18839 6, price (in UK only) £4.99, printed on recycled paper.
'... Essential reading.' *Daily Mirror*

OTHER GREEN BOOKS

New Green Pages: A Directory of Natural Products, Services, Resources and Ideas compiled by **John Button**
ISBN 0 356 19109 5, price (in UK only) £11.99, printed on recycled paper.
'... an absolute must for the all-round green consumer.'
Nineteen

Green Parenting by **Juliet Solomon**
ISBN 0 356 18768 3, price (in UK only) £6.99, printed on recycled paper.
Selected as one of the Green Book Fortnight's Top Twelve Titles in 1990.

A Green Manifesto by Sandy Irvine and Alec Ponton
ISBN 0 356 15200 6, price (in UK only) £6.99.
Selected as one of the Green Book Fortnight's Top Twenty
Titles in 1989.
'... not just another book about the state of the
environment ... a hard-headed presentation of radical
alternatives, based on a fundamental reinterpretation of
the relationship between humankind and plant Earth.'
Jonathon Porritt

Guide to Gaia by Michael Allaby
ISBN 0 356 17535 9, price (in UK only) £6.99
An introduction to the Gaia hypothesis, and the way it can
be used to look at environmental problems.

The Future is Now by Deirdre Rhys-Thomas
ISBN 0 356 17947 8, price (in UK only) £4.99, printed on
recycled paper.
Leading personalities from public affairs, the media,
science and the health professions voice their concerns
about the environmental dangers facing the planet.

Down the Drain: Water, Pollution and Privatisation
by Stuart Gordon
ISBN 0 356 17944 3, price (in UK only) £5.99
A searching – and disturbing –investigation of the use and
abuse of our most valuable natural resource – water.

The Allotment Book by Rob Bullock and Gillie Gould
ISBN 0 356 12890 3, price (in UK only) £4.95
Recommended on BBC Radio 4's *Gardeners' Question
Time*

Cheaper and Better by Nancy Birnes
ISBN 0 356 15555 2, price (in UK only) £3.99

Pay Less, Keep Warm by Barty Phillips
ISBN 0 356 12889 X, price (in UK only) £4.95

Alternative Maternity by Nicky Wesson
ISBN 0 356 15412 2, price (in UK only) £5.99

Home Birth by Nicky Wesson
ISBN 0 356 17491 3, price (in UK only) £6.99

RECENTLY PUBLISHED

Green Dictionary by Colin Johnson
ISBN 0 356 19568 6, price (in UK only) £9.99

The Energy Alternative by Walter C. Patterson
ISBN 0 356 20040 X, price (in UK only) £5.99
'... The wit and infectious enthusiasm of Walter C.
Patterson's writing brings this subject to life ... creating a
captivating adventure of a book.' Simon Roberts, Friends
of the Earth

Solar-Hydrogen Energy: The Power to save the Earth
by Professor John O'M. Bockris and Professor T. Nejat
Vezirogly with Debbi Smith
ISBN 0 356 20042 6, price (in UK only) £7.99

All Optima books are available at your bookshop or
newsagent, or can be ordered from the following address:

Optima, Cash Sales Department,
PO Box 11, Falmouth, Cornwall TR10 9EN

Please send cheque or postal order (no currency), and
allow 60p for postage and packing for the first book, plus
25p for the second book and 15p for each additional book
ordered up to a maximum charge of £1.90 in the UK.

Customers in Eire and BFPO please allow 60p for the first
book, 25p for the second book plus 15p per copy for the
next 7 books, thereafter 9p per book.

Overseas customers please allow £1.25 for postage and
packing for the first book and 28p per copy for each
additional book.

INDEX

INDEX

threat to wildlife, 43, 45–7; water
pollution, 48, 49
pests and diseases: crop rotations, 72;
non-chemical control, 72–4;
organic gardening, 139–46
phosphates, 48
pigs, 39, 58, 59, 60
plants: air pollution, 50; loss of
habitats, 45
pollution: air, 49–53; rivers, 47–9
polyphosphates, 25
polyunsaturated fats, 30
population growth, 63
potatoes, 18, 107
poultry: free range, 57–8; intensive
farming, 55, 57, 60; salmonella,
33–4; water content, 25–6
predators, pest control, 72–3
preservatives, 20; irradiation, 28–31;
salt as, 25
prices, organic food, 109
processed foods, 37–8, 97–8
productivity, organic farming, 102–12
propiniates, 21
PST (porcine somatotropin), 39, 40
pulses, pesticide residues, 16
pyrethrum, 74, 145

quassia chips, 145

radioactivity, 30
rain, acid, 50
rainforests, 65–7
recycling nutrients, 74–5, 130
refined foods, 37–8, 97–8
refrigerators, 34
regional guides, Soil Association,
123–4
residues, pesticides, 11–16, 96
rice, 16, 68, 84
rivers, 47–9
Rose, Sir Julian, 99
rotation of crops, 72, 127, 137–9
roughage, 37
Royal Society for the Protection of
Birds, 46

Safeways, 125
Sainsburys, 125
salads, 34, 79
salmonella, 30, 33–4, 58, 60
salt, 22, 24–5, 97
saturated fats, 38, 97
scrapie, 35
seaweed, 22
'set aside' schemes, 105

Severn Trent Water Authority, 47–8
sewage sludge, 75
sheep, 61, 107; dipping, 81, 86, 120;
scrapie, 35
shops, organic food, 122–5
silage, 49
simazine, 49
slaughterhouses, 32–3, 61
slugs, 136, 140, 142, 144
slurry, 17, 48–9, 53
Society for the Protection of Ancient
Buildings, 94
soil: acidification, 51; crop rotations,
72, 127, 137–9; erosion, 2, 53–4,
89; improving fertility 130–9;
organic farming, 74–6, 88–9;
organic gardening, 128–37; under
rainforests, 65
Soil Association: campaign against
nitrates, 19; Campaign for Safe
Meat, 55–6; certification of organic
food, 115–17; Charter on Animal
Feeds, 36; Charter for Organic
Agriculture, 77–8; creation and
aims, 1–8; Crisis in the
Countryside campaign, 44–5; and
food additives, 97; foreign
verification scheme, 84, 119; and
pesticide residues, 14–15; regional
guides, 123–4; research into
erosion, 53–4; standards and
symbol, 97, 115, 117–21, 123–4;
third world education project, 111;
20 per cent by 2000 campaign,
107–8, 110; and use of antibiotics,
28; wildlife conservation, 90–4
Soilwatch, 54
spices, irradiation, 29
spinach, 17, 19
spray drift, pesticides, 14, 15,
51–2
SSSIs (sites of special scientific
interest), 44
stearates, 21
Steinbeck, John, 2
stomach cancer, 18–19
straw burning, 47
stress, farm animals, 59–60, 61
Strutt Report, 53
sugar, 22–4, 97
sugar beet, 107
sulphur dioxide, 50
synergism, 50–1

tea, 84, 119
Tescos, 125

INDEX

third world countries, 63–5, 102–3, 110–11
tinned foods, 23, 25
toads, 140–2
transport, farm animals, 61
traps, peat control, 144
trees: acid rain, 50; conifers, 43, 44; on organic farms, 92–3; rainforests, 65–7; woodlands, 43, 92–3
turkeys, 57

United Kingdom Register of Organic Food Standards (UKROFS), 120
United Nations, 15, 111
United States Department of Agriculture, 89
United States Environmental Protection Agency, 13
urine, 134

veal crates, 58
Vegan Society, 101
vegans, 100–1
vegetables: crop rotation, 137–9; fibre content, 37; irradiation, 29, 30; nitrate levels, 17–19; organic farming, 79; pesticide residues, 11–16; tinned, 23, 25; water content, 26

vegetarians, 55, 83, 100–1
Veterinary Advisory Committee, 39
veterinary surgeons, 27–8, 32, 81
vitamins, 19, 30, 37, 99

Waldersteben, 50, 53
water: acid rain, 50; artificial addition to food, 25–6; water filters, 19; irrigation, 63–4; nitrate levels, 16, 17, 18, 19, 87; river pollution, 47–9
Webb, Tony, 30
weeds, 73, 130, 131, 134, 139, 144–5
wetlands, 45, 92
wheat, irradiation, 29–30
wholefoods, pesticide residues, 16
Wholefood (organic shop), 122
wildlife: organic farming and, 89–94; threats to, 45–7
Wilson, Donald, 122
wine, organic, 82–3, 124
woodlands, 43, 92–3
World Health Organisation (WHO), 17, 25, 29
worms, 130, 135
Wright, Iain, 124

yoghurt, 23

zineb, 13

HELP US TO TURN BRITAIN ORGANIC

"Intensive agriculture in the UK is contributing to the destruction of our environment and the contamination of our food."

IT DOESN'T HAVE TO BE LIKE THAT

Organic agriculture is an environmentally friendly way of producing high quality, healthy food by crop rotation and natural inputs, whilst treating farm animals with real concern for their well being. It treats nature as an ally, not as an enemy.

- The Soil Association plays a key role in promoting organic farming with producers, consumers, retailers and policy makers.

- It exposes problems connected with food, health and the environment.

- It sets and administers the Soil Association Symbol, which ensures that organic food is produced to the highest quality.

The Soil Association needs your help with the immense task of promoting organic agriculture.

Become a member and receive our quarterly magazine "Living Earth", details of our network of local groups and specialised book and information services. You will also receive regular details of our campaigns.

- -

HOW YOU CAN HELP

1. BECOME A MEMBER

£12 Individual ☐   £8 Student, OAP or unwaged ☐   £20 Overseas ☐

2. GIVE A DONATION

£100 ☐   £50 ☐   £20 ☐   other ☐   CAT91

Name _____

Address _____

_____ Postcode _____

PLEASE PRINT IN BLOCK CAPITALS

(Cheques/POs payable The Soil Association)

PLEASE RETURN TO THE SOIL ASSOCIATION, FREEPOST, BRISTOL BS1 5YZ